Talk To Me In Korean
Workbook
Level 5

written by
TalkToMeInKorean

Talk To Me In Korean Workbook (Level 5)

| 1판 1쇄 | 1st edition published | 2018. 5. 14 |
| 1판 6쇄 | 6th edition published | 2020. 9. 7 |

지은이	Written by	TalkToMeInKorean
책임편집	Edited by	선경화 Kyung-hwa Sun, 에밀리 프리즈러키 Emily Przylucki
디자인	Designed by	선윤아 Yoona Sun
삽화	Illustrations by	까나리 존스 Sungwon Jang
녹음	Voice Recordings by	선경화 Kyung-hwa Sun
펴낸곳	Published by	롱테일북스 Longtail Books
펴낸이	Publisher	이수영 Su Young Lee
편집	Copy-edited by	김보경 Florence Kim
주소	Address	04043 서울 마포구 양화로 12길 16-9(서교동) 북앤빌딩 3층 롱테일북스
		3rd Floor Book-And Bldg. 16-9 Yanghwa-ro 12-gil, Mapo-gu, Seoul, KOREA
이메일	E-mail	TTMIK@longtailbooks.co.kr
ISBN		979-11-86701-14-0 14710

*이 교재의 내용을 사전 허가 없이 전재하거나 복제할 경우 법적인 제재를 받게 됨을 알려 드립니다.

*잘못된 책은 구입하신 서점이나 본사에서 교환해 드립니다.

*정가는 표지에 표시되어 있습니다.

TTMIK - TALK TO ME IN KOREAN

Talk To Me In Korean Workbook

Level 5

Contents

How to Use
the Talk To Me In Korean Workbook

This workbook is designed to be used in conjunction with the Talk To Me In Korean Level 5 lessons, which are available for free at TalkToMeInKorean.com. You can also purchase the paperback book of the Talk To Me In Korean Level 5 lessons at MyKoreanStore.com. Developed by certified teachers to help you review and reinforce what you've learned, each lesson in this workbook contains three to five activity sections, chosen from 3 main review categories and 15 types of exercises:

Categories

1. Vocabulary
2. Comprehension
3. Listening Comprehension

Types of Exercises

1. Matching
2. Translation Practice
3. Fill in the Blank
4. Short Answer
5. Multiple Choice
6. Conjugation Practice
7. Complete the Dialogue
8. Checking for Understanding

9. Writing Practice

10. Fill in the Chart

11. Paraphrasing

12. Reading

13. Contraction Practice

14. Expansion Practice

15. Quoting

 The "Listening Comprehension" category is designed to aid in developing your Korean listening skills. Listen to the corresponding audio file and answer the question. In order to get the most benefit from this category, you should download the available audio files from *www.talktomeinkorean.com/audio*. These files are in MP3 format and are free of cost.

Section I – Vocabulary

Match each Korean word/phrase to its common English translation. All words and phrases are used in the following sections, so be sure to commit them to memory!

1. 차에 치이다

    a. to get into an accident

2. 사고(가) 나다

    b. to get caught

3. 말하다

    c. to miss the train

4. 기차를 놓치다

    d. to fall off a chair

5. 울다

    e. to get hit by a car

6. 들키다/잡히다

    f. to say/tell/speak/talk

7. 죽다

    g. to die

8. 의자에서 떨어지다

    h. to cry

Section II - Translation Practice

Translate the sentences into Korean using -(으)ㄹ 뻔했다.

9. I almost died. =

10. I almost cried. =

11. I almost said it. =

12. I almost got caught. =

13. I almost got hit by a car. =

14. I almost fell off the chair. =

15. I almost missed the train. =

16. I almost got into an accident. =

Rewrite the sentences by adding the adverb 하마터면 at the beginning. 하마터면 is often used with -(으)ㄹ 뻔했다 to emphasize how close something was actually about to happen without adding any additional meaning.

9a.

10a

11a.

12a.

13a.

14a.

15a.

16a.

Section III - Listening Comprehension

Listen to the dialogue and fill in the blanks with the missing word/phrase. The dialogue will be played twice.

A: 아! 정말 아쉬워요.

B: 왜요?

A: 달리기 일 등 할 17. (   ), 넘어져서 오 등 했어요.

B: 진짜요? 저는 18. (   ), 안 넘어졌어요.

You can download the mp3 audio files at: www.talktomeinkorean.com/audio

Lesson 2.
Honorific Suffix: -시-

Section I - Comprehension
Answer the following questions.

1. What is the honorific suffix that is combined with verbs in order for the speaker to show respect for the person about whom he/she is talking?

2. When you want to politely address someone using 존댓말, you should add the word 씨 after their name. What is the particle that you use in the title of a person's job or status, that is a higher honorific than 씨?

3. In casual conversations, adding -이 or -가 as subject markers is acceptable, but when using honorifics, to what do you change -이 or -가?

4. When –시– is combined with –아/어/여요, it becomes –셔요. However, Korean people don't really use this form in present tense sentences and imperative sentences anymore. What do they use instead?

5. Which one is the most natural/correct honorific sentence?

   a. 말씀해!

   b. 먹으세요.

   c. 아빠가 보샀어요.

   d. 이거 보실 거예요?

Section II - Conjugation Practice

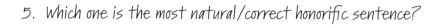

Change the following phrases/sentences to the honorific form by adding –시–.

6. 먹어도 ⟶

7. 좋아해서 ⟶

8. 들어와요. ⟶

9. 어디 가요? ↣

10. 물 마실래요? ↣

11. 선생님 왔어요. ↣

12. 지금 보면 안 돼요. ↣

13. 이 책상 팔 거예요? ↣

Section III - Listening Comprehension

Listen to the dialogue and fill in the blanks with the missing word/phrase. The dialogue will be played twice.

A: 안녕하세요.

B: 안녕하세요. 사장님 어디 14. (   )?

A: 손님 15. (   ) 잠깐 16. (   ).

Lesson 3. Good work
수고

Section I - Comprehension

Multiple choice. Circle the best answer.

1. What does 수고 literally mean?

    a. Thank you

    b. Goodbye

    c. Hard work

    d. Congratulations

2. When a customer leaves a store in Korea, which of the following expressions does the customer say as a farewell?

    a. 수고하셨습니다.

    b. 수고했어요.

    c. 수고했어.

    d. 수고하세요.

3. Which of the following expressions sounds rudest when spoken to someone much older?

    a. 수고하셨습니다.

    b. 수고하세요.

    c. 안녕히 계세요.

    d. 수고 많으셨습니다.

4. Which of the following expressions cannot be said to someone who just finished a task?

   a. 수고 많았어.

   b. 수고했어.

   c. 수고했어요.

   d. 수고해요.

5. List the following expressions from most polite to least polite.

   수고했어요   수고했어   수고하셨습니다

   a. 수고했어, 수고했어요, 수고하셨습니다

   b. 수고했어, 수고하셨습니다, 수고했어요

   c. 수고하셨습니다, 수고했어, 수고했어요

   d. 수고하셨습니다, 수고했어요, 수고했어

Section II - Listening Comprehension

Listen to the dialogue and answer the following questions. The
dialogue will be played twice.

6. Between the man and the woman, who is older or in a higher position than
   the other?

7. Which of the following statements is true?

    a. The man is in the middle of recording.

    b. The woman is about to record.

    c. The man is about to record.

    d. The woman is in the middle of recording.

Section I - Vocabulary

Create a Korean phrase by matching a word on the left with the most appropriate word on the right, and write it on the line on the next page. Choose the most accurate English translation from the "Translation Bank" and write it next to the Korean phrase. The first one has been done for you.

Translation Bank

to walk quickly	to live with one's parents	Jooyeon and Kyung-hwa meet
to rain	to stay close to (someone)	to study at home
there is no one/nobody	to like snacks	

1.	집에서		좋아하다
2.	주연 씨랑 경화 씨랑		없다
3.	친하게		살다
4.	빨리		공부하다
5.	과자를		걷다
6.	부모님이랑		만나나
7.	아무도		오다
8.	비가		지내다

1. 집에서 공부하다 = to study at home

_____

2.

_____

3.

_____

4.

_____

5.

_____

6.

_____

7.

_____

8.

_____

Section II - Tense Conjugation

Use the phrases from Section I – Vocabulary and conjugate them into present tense and past tense with -나 보다. After completing each sentence, translate it into your preferred language (translations in the Answer Key are given in English).

1a.

[Present tense] >> 경은 씨는 주로 _____ .

=

[Past tense] >> 주말에 _____ 열심히 _____ .

=

2a.

[Present tense] >> _____ 자주 _____ .

=

[Past tense] >> _____ 어제 _____ .

=

3a.

[Present tense] >> 우진이가 학교에서 친구들이랑 _____ .

=

[Past tense] >> 우진이가 종현이랑 제일 _____ .

=

4a.

[Present tense] >> 제가 너무 ‿‿‿‿‿‿‿‿‿‿‿‿‿‿‿‿‿‿‿‿‿ .

=

[Past tense] >> 제가 너무 ‿‿‿‿‿‿‿‿‿‿‿‿‿‿‿‿‿‿‿‿‿‿ .

=

5a.

[Present tense] >> 현우 씨는 ‿‿‿‿‿‿‿‿‿‿‿‿‿‿‿‿‿‿‿‿ .

=

[Past tense] >> 어렸을 때 ‿‿‿‿‿‿‿‿‿‿‿‿‿‿‿‿‿‿‿‿‿ .

=

6a.

[Present tense] >> 석진 씨는 아직도 ‿‿‿‿‿‿‿‿‿‿‿‿‿‿‿‿ .

=

[Past tense] >> 그때는 ‿‿‿‿‿‿‿‿‿‿‿‿‿‿‿‿‿‿‿‿‿‿ .

=

7a.

[Present tense] >> (똑똑) 저기요! 여기 〰〰〰〰〰〰〰〰〰〰〰〰〰〰.

=

[Past tense] >> 택배 왔을 때 집에 〰〰〰〰〰〰〰〰〰〰〰〰〰〰〰.

=

8a.

[Present tense] >> 지금 밖에 〰〰〰〰〰〰〰 많이 〰〰〰〰〰〰〰〰.

=

[Past tense] >> 새벽에 〰〰〰〰〰〰〰〰〰〰〰〰〰〰〰〰〰〰.

=

Section III - Listening Comprehension

Listen to the dialogue and fill in the blanks with the missing word/ phrase. The dialogue will be played twice.

A: 저기 무슨 행사 9. (　　　　　　　　　). 사람들이 많이 모여 있어요.

B: 한번 가 볼까요?

A: 아! 다 10. (　　　　　　　).

Section I - Vocabulary

Use a dictionary to find out the part of speech for each word, then define/translate it into English. All words and phrases are used in the following sections, so be sure to commit them to memory!

1. 똑똑하다 _____

2. 잘하다 _____

3. 궁금하다 _____

4. 어색하다 _____

5. 기대하다 _____

6. 힘들다 _____

7. 여동생 _____

8. 초인종 _____

9. 누르다 _____

10. 답 _____

Section II - Grammar Point Comprehension

Multiple choice. Circle the best answer.

11. Which of the following words CANNOT be conjugated with -(으)ㄴ가 보다?

    a. 똑똑하다

    b. 공부하다

    c. 바쁘다

    d. 비싸다

12. Which of the following words can be conjugated with both -(으)ㄴ가 보다 and -나 보다 in everyday conversation?

    a. 기다리다

    b. 재미있다

    c. 어렵다

    d. 잘하다

13. Which of the following words CANNOT be conjugated with -나 보다?

    a. 재미없다   b. 자다   c. 귀엽다   d. 크다

14. Which conjugation is incorrect?

    a. 궁금한가 봐요.

    b. 어색한가 봐요.

    c. 기대한가 봐요.

    d. 힘든가 봐요.

15. Which of the following sounds most unnatural?

    a. 최경은 선생님이 영어 선생님인가 봐요.

    b. 석진 씨가 여동생이 있나 봐요.

    c. 현우 씨가 감기에 걸렸나 봐요.

    d. 저는 오늘 일찍 집에 갔나 봐요.

Section III - Conjugation Practice

Conjugate the following verbs with either -나 보다 or -(으)ㄴ가 보다 in the present tense, and translate the sentences into English and/or your preferred language (translations in the Answer Key are given in English). Use the verb 하다 (= to do) for all exercises.

    Ex)
    하다 + -(으)ㄹ 수 있다 + -나 보다 *or* -(으)ㄴ가 보다:
    할 수 있나 봐요. = *I guess he/she can do (it).*

16. 하다 + -고 싶어요 + -나 보다 *or* -(으)ㄴ가 보다:

17. 하다 + -고 있다 + -나 보다 *or* -(으)ㄴ가 보다:

18. 하다 + -지 않다 + -나 보다 *or* -(으)ㄴ가 보다:

19. 하다 + -게 되다 + -나 보다 *or* -(으)ㄴ가 보다:

20. 하다 + -(으)ㄹ 수 없다 + -나 보다 *or* -(으)ㄴ가 보다:

21. 하다 + -아/어/여야 하다 + -나 보다 *or* -(으)ㄴ가 보다:

22. 하다 + -아/어/여도 되다 + -나 보다 *or* -(으)ㄴ가 보다:

23. 하다 + -(으)면 안 되다 + -나 보다 *or* -(으)ㄴ가 보다:

Section IV - Listening Comprehension

Listen to the dialogue and fill in the blanks with the missing word/phrase. The dialogue will be played twice.

A: 석진 씨가 24. (   ).

B: 왜요? 답이 없어요?

A: 네. 초인종을 여러 번 눌렀는데 아무도 안 나와요.

B: 분명히 집에 있는데… 아마 25. (   ).

Section I - Vocabulary, Part 1

Translate each word into English using what you know, Talk To Me In Korean Level 5 Lesson 6, or a dictionary, then define it in your preferred language (if not English). Translations in the Answer Key are given in English.

1. 문화(文化) _____

2. 문서(文書) _____

3. 문장(文章) _____

4. 문자(文字) _____

5. 문학(文學) _____

6. 문법(文法) _____

7. 주문(注文) _____

8. 논문(論文) _____

9. 문화재(文化財) _____

Section II - Vocabulary, Part 2

Choose a word from Section I – Vocabulary Part I and write it in the most appropriate box to match the English definition. Each word is used only once.

10. 인간 ☐☐☐ = human cultural assets

11. 영국 ☐☐ = English literature

12. 고대 ☐☐ = ancient character/letter

13. ☐☐ 번호 = order number

14. 한국어 ☐☐ = Korean sentence

15. 한국 ☐☐ = Korean culture

16. 새 ☐☐ = new document

17. ☐☐ 제출했어요? = Have you submitted your thesis?

18. ☐☐ 공부하는 거 싫어해요. = I hate studying grammar.

Section III – Listening Comprehension

Listen to the dialogue and fill in the blanks with the missing word/phrase. The dialogue will be played twice.

A: 오늘 주문 19. (   ) 거 있어요?

B: 아직 없어요.

A: 주문 20. (   ) 문서에 21. (   ) 주세요.

B: 네.

Lesson 7.
As soon as ...
-자마자

Section I - Vocabulary

Review the vocabulary words from Talk To Me In Korean Level 5 Lesson 7 by translating them into English.

1. 잠들다

_____

2. 일

_____

3. 시작하다

_____

4. 전화하다

_____

5. 마음에 들다

_____

6. 다시

_____

7. 나오다

_____

Section II - Conjugation Practice

Complete the sentences by conjugating the word provided in the parentheses with -자마자, then translate each sentence into English.

8. ～～～～～～～～～～ 전화할게요. (도착하다)

=

9. ～～～～～～～～～ 전화를 했어요. (가다)

=

10. ～～～～～～～～～ 다시 나왔어요. (들어가다)

=

11. ～～～～～～～～ 마음에 들었어요. (보다)

=

12. 집에 ～～～～～～～～ 잠들었어요. (오다)

=

13. ～～～～～～～～ 일을 시작할 거예요. (졸업하다)

=

Section III - Listening Comprehension

Listen to the dialogue and fill in the blanks with the missing word/ phrase. The dialogue will be played twice.

A: 은지 씨, 은지 씨는 회사에 14. (   ) 바로 일 시작해요?

B: 네. 대신 퇴근 시간 15. (   ) 퇴근해요.

Lesson 8.
It is about to ...,
I am planning to ...

-(으)려고 하다

Section I - Vocabulary

Match each Korean word/phrase to its common English translation. All words and phrases are used in the following sections, so be sure to commit them to memory!

1. 혼자

2. 출발하다

3. 축구(를) 하다

4. 동물원

5. 공

6. 취소되다

7. 배낭여행

8. 냉장고

9. 선수

10. 손님

a. customer

b. refrigerator

c. by oneself

d. to play soccer

e. backpacking trip

f. to depart, to leave

g. zoo

h. to be canceled

i. ball

j. player

Section II - Comprehension

-(으)려고 하다 has two usages: showing an intention to do an action, or talking about the state of the near future based on your assumptions or judgements. Write S if the -(으)려고 하다 in the sentence is "showing an intention to do an action" and T if it is "talking about a state of the near future".

11. 친구가 울려고 해요. (   )

12. 이번 주말에 동물원에 가려고 해요. (   )

13. 유럽으로 배낭여행을 가려고 해요. (   )

14. 아이스크림이 녹으려고 해요. (   )

15. 비가 오려고 해요. (   )

16. 새 냉장고를 사려고 해요. (   )

Section III - Conjugation Practice

-(으)려고 하다 is often used with -(으/느)ㄴ데. Fill in the blanks using the word/phrase in parentheses + -(으)려고 하다 + -(으/느)ㄴ데. Translate each sentence into English and/or your preferred language (translations in the Answer Key are given in English).

[Present tense]

17. (출발하다)

지금 (   ), 석진 씨가 아직 안 왔어요.

=

18. (시험을 보다)

TOPIK (   ), 혼자 공부해도 될까요?

=

19. (사다)

카메라 (   ), 뭐가 좋아요?

=

[Past tense]

20. (만나다)

어제 친구 (   ), 못 만났어요.

=

21. (참다)

(   ) 너무 배고파서 먼저 먹었어요.

=

22. (축구 하다)

친구들이랑 (   ) 비가 와서 취소됐어요.

=

Section IV - Fill in the Blank

Complete the phrases below by conjugating -(으)려고 하다 correctly.

23. (   ) 친구 = a friend who is planning to move

24. 외국에서 (   ) 학생들 = students who are planning
    to study abroad

25. 공을 (   ) 선수 = a player who is about to catch a ball

26. 밥을 (   ) 사람 = a person who is going to have a meal
    / a person who is about to have a meal

27. 가방을 (   ) 손님 = a customer who is planning to buy
    a bag / a customer who is about to buy a bag

Section V - Listening Comprehension

Listen to the dialogue and fill in the blanks with the missing word/
phrase. The dialogue will be played twice.

A: 왜 방문을 닫아 놨어요?

B: 강아지가 자꾸 28. (   ) 해서요.

A: 그래도 막 29. (   ) 하지 않아요?

Lesson 9.
While I was doing ...,
... and then ...

-다가

Section I - Vocabulary

Match each Korean word/phrase to its common English translation. All words and phrases are used in the following sections, so be sure to commit them to memory!

1. 계속

a. to call, to invite

2. 최근에

b. to solve

3. 고르다

c. continuously

4. 고민하다

d. recently

5. 부르다

e. to be tiring, to be hard

6. 풀다

f. to work part-time

7. 지나가다

g. to choose

8. 아르바이트하다

h. to mull over, to contemplate

9. 힘들다

i. to quit

10. 그만두다

j. to pass (by)

Section II - Writing Practice

Combine the two sentences into one, as seen in the example.

Ex) 여행을 하고 있었어요. 감기에 걸렸어요.

→ 여행을 하다가 감기에 걸렸어요. (= I was traveling and I caught a cold.)

11. 서울에서 살고 있었어요. 제주도로 이사 갔어요.

→

12. 밥 먹고 있었어요. 전화를 받았어요.

→

13. 집에서 공부하고 있었어요. 나왔어요.

→

14. 텔레비전을 보고 있었어요. 잠이 들었어요.

→

15. 집에 오고 있었어요. 친구를 만났어요.

→

Talk To Me In Korean Workbook

Section III - Complete the Dialogue

Complete the dialogues by conjugating the verbs in the parentheses using -다가 -아/어/여서 -았/었/였어요, then translate them into your preferred language (translations in the Answer Key are given in English). An example has been provided.

Ex)

A: 왜 들어왔어요? = Why did you come in?

B: 밖에 있다가 추워서 들어왔어요. (있다, 춥다, 들어오다)

= I was outside, but then it was cold, so I came in.

16. A: 왜 이거 골랐어요? =

B: 계속 _____ 이게 제일 _____.

(고민하다, 싸다, 고르다)

=

17. A: 어제 집에 혼자 있었어요? =

B: 혼자 _____ 너무 _____ 친구를 _____.

(있다, 무섭다, 부르다)

=

18. A: 선생님한테 뭐 물어봤어요? =

B: 수학 문제를 _____ 너무 _____.

(풀다, 어렵다, 물어보다)

=

19. A: 어서 오세요. =

B: 안녕하세요. ＿＿＿＿＿＿＿ 옷이 너무 ＿＿＿＿＿＿＿＿＿＿＿＿ .

(지나가다, 예쁘다, 들어오다)

=

20. A: 요즘 어떻게 지내요? =

B: 계속 ＿＿＿＿＿＿ 너무 ＿＿＿＿＿＿ 최근에 ＿＿＿＿＿＿ .

(아르바이트하다, 힘들다, 그만두다)

=

Section IV - Listening Comprehension

Listen to the dialogue and fill in the blanks with the missing word/phrase. The dialogue will be played twice.

A: 늦어서 죄송해요.

B: 뭐 21. (   ) 이렇게 늦게 왔어요?

A: 지하철에서 22. (   ) 잘못 내렸어요.

Section I - Vocabulary

Multiple choice. Circle the best answer.

1. The Korean word for "later" is:

   a. 나징에   *b.* 이따가   *c.* 더 늦게   *d.* none of these

2. 아무거나 means:

   a. anything; doesn't matter what

   b. anybody; doesn't matter who; anyone

   c. nobody; not anybody

   d. nothing; not anything

3. How do you say "wallet" in Korean?

   a. 가방   *b.* 웰렛   *c.* 지갑   *d.* 돈

4. To say "anywhere" or "any place" in Korean, you use the word:

   a. 아무한테도

   b. 아무렇게나

   c. 아무 때나

   d. 아무 데나

5. The correct translation for the Korean word "일 등" is:

    a. one person

    b. one back

    c. the first place winner

    d. none of the above

6. 놀이공원 translates to English as:

    a. play park

    b. playground

    c. fun park

    d. theme park

7. What is 범인 in English?

    a. criminal, culprit

    b. vomit

    c. president

    d. police officer

8. What does 선물 mean?

    a. present, gift

    b. pay

    c. money

    d. cash

Assume that the person from whom you heard and the person to whom you are speaking are both your close friends. Write down a direct speech sentence using quotation marks in 반말, casual language. The first one has been done for you.

9. 민호가 "이따가 전화할게." 라고 했어.

민호: 이따가 전화할게.

10.

수정: 수업 시작하기 전에 올게.

11.

두준: 나는 아무거나 줘도 돼.

12.

슬기: 나는 아무데나 괜찮아.

공명

나는 여름보다 겨울
이 훨씬 더 좋아.

Me

13.

하나

이 드라마 좀
재밌네.

Me

14.

Section III - Conjugation Practice II

Change the sentences to a negative, then translate each sentence into English and your preferred language (if not English).

Ex) 학생이라고 말하다 = to say that (someone) is a student

➜ 학생이 아니라고 말하다 = to say that (someone) is not a student

15. 공짜라고 말하다

➜

16. 한국 사람이라고 말하다

➜

17. 내 지갑이라고 말하다

    ⤙

18. 범인이라고 말하다

    ⤙

19. 일 등이라고 듣다

    ⤙

20. 선물이라고 듣다

    ⤙

Section IV - Listening Comprehension

Listen to the dialogue and fill in the blanks with the missing word/ phrase. The dialogue will be played twice.

A: 주연 씨, 내일 21. (   ).

B: 네, 맞아요. 친구랑 놀이공원 가요.

A: 아! 친구도 내일 22. (   )?

B: 네. 그 친구도 내일 쉬어요.

Lesson 11.
Sentence Building Drill #3

Section I - Vocabulary

Match each Korean word/phrase to its common English translation. All words and phrases are used in the following sections, so be sure to commit them to memory!

1. 반하다

2. 추천하다

3. 달려가다

4. 마음에 들다

5. 인기가 많다

6. 일 등 하다

7. 떨어뜨리다

8. 고장 나다

9. 손님

10. 소식

a. to rank first, to win first place

b. to drop (something)

c. news

d. to recommend

e. to fall in love

f. to run

g. to break down, to stop working

h. to be popular

i. to like

j. customer, guest

Section II – Conjugation Practice

The following exercises use all of the grammar points that you have learned so far. Complete the sentences using the grammar point and the words given in the parentheses. An example has been provided.

-아/어/여서 -자마자 -았/었/였어요. = …, so as soon as I/we [verb], I/we [verb].

Example: (마음에 들다, 보다, 사다)

가방이 너무 마음에 들어서 보자마자 샀어요.

(= I really liked the bag, so I bought it as soon as I saw it.)

11. (예쁘다, 보다, 반하다)

태희 씨가 너무 〰〰〰〰〰〰〰〰〰〰〰〰〰〰〰〰〰〰 .

12. (아프다, 타다, 앉다)

다리가 너무 〰〰〰〰〰〰 지하철을 〰〰〰〰〰〰〰〰〰 .

13. (놀라다, 듣다, 전화하다)

너무 〰〰〰〰〰 그 소식을 〰〰〰〰〰 규리 씨한테 〰〰〰〰〰〰〰 .

14. (재미있다, 읽다, 추천하다)

그 책이 너무 〰〰〰〰〰 다 〰〰〰〰〰 친구한테 〰〰〰〰〰〰〰 .

15. (많다, 되다, 달려가다)

그 식당이 인기가 너무 ～～～～～～ 점심시간 ～～～～～～～～～～～～～.

-아/어/여서 -(으)ㄴ/는 것 같아요. = I think... because...

　　Example: (지치다, 가다)
　　기다리다가 지쳐서 간 것 같아요. [past tense]
　　(= I think he/she left because he/she got tired/exhausted after wait-
　　ing.)

16. (좋다, 많다)

노래가 ～～～～～～ 인기가 ～～～～～～. [present tense]

17. (하다, 하다)

공부를 열심히 ～～～～～～ 일 등 ～～～～～～. [past tense]

18. (안 일어나다, 안 받다)

아직 ～～～～～～ 전화를 ～～～～～～. [present tense]

19. (떨어뜨리다, 고장 나다)

제가 핸드폰을 계속 ～～～～～～ ～～～～～～. [past tense]

20. (춥다, 없다)

오늘 날씨가 너무 ～～～～～～～ 손님이 별로 ～～～～～～～. [present tense]

Section III - Listening Comprehension

Listen to the sentences and fill in the blanks with the missing word/phrase. Each sentence will be played twice.

21. 이 중에서 아무거나 (   )?

22. 어제 너무 (   ) 집에 가자마자 아무것도 (   ) 바로

    잠들었어요.

23. 날씨가 더워서 사람들이 별로 (   ).

Lesson 12.
-(이)라는
Noun + that is called / that people say is + noun

Section I - Vocabulary

Match each Korean word to its common English translation. All words are used in the following section, so be sure to commit them to memory!

1. 야구 선수   a. student

2. 사람   b. actor/actress

3. 식당   c. baseball player

4. 질문   d. restaurant

5. 가수   e. thing

6. 학생   f. person

7. 배우   g. question

8. 것   h. singer

Section II - Translation Practice

Translate each phrase into Korean using -(이)라는. Use the words from Section I - Vocabulary.

9. Lee So Ra = 이소라

   the singer called Lee So Ra =

10. Lee Jong Wook = 이종욱

    the baseball player named Lee Jong Wook =

11. Kim Ji Eun = 김지은

    the student called Kim Ji Eun =

12. Gimbap Heaven = 김밥 천국

    the restaurant called Gimbap Heaven =

13. Bae Doona = 배두나

    the actress called Bae Doona =

14. Choi Kyeong Eun = 최경은

    the person named Choi Kyeong Eun =

15. destiny = 운명

    the thing called destiny =

16. What is the most difficult (thing)? = 뭐가 제일 어려워요?

the question that asks "What is the most difficult (thing)?"

=

Section III - Vocabulary

Match each Korean word/phrase to its common English translation. All words and phrases are used in the following section, so be sure to commit them to memory!

17. 들어 보다   a. Korean language

18. 여러 가지   b. to come and hang out

19. 뜻   c. many, a lot of

20. 놀러 오다   d. to teach

21. 한국어   e. meaning

22. 가르치다   f. to try and listen, to have heard

Section IV - Comprehension

Complete the sentences by choosing the most appropriate word from the box + -(이)라는. Each word is used only once.

친구	선생님	영화
노래	말	웹사이트

23. 싸이(PSY)의 강남스타일 ＿＿＿＿＿ 들어 봤어요?

24. 주말에 올드보이(Oldboy) ＿＿＿＿＿ 를 봤어요.

25. "괜찮아요." ＿＿＿＿＿ 은 여러 가지 뜻이 있어요.

26. TalkToMeInKorean.com(톡투미인코리안닷컴) ＿＿＿＿＿ 알아요?

27. 내일 알렉스 ＿＿＿＿＿ 가 놀러 올 거예요.

28. 선현우 ＿＿＿＿＿ 이 한국어를 가르치고 있어요.

Section V - Listening Comprehension

Listen to the sentence and fill in the blank with the missing word/phrase. The sentence will be played twice.

29. (＿＿＿＿＿) 재미없으면 오래 할 수 없어요.

Section I - Vocabulary

Translate each word into English using what you know, Talk To Me In Korean Level 5 Lesson 13, or a dictionary, then define it in your preferred language (if not English). Translations in the Answer Key are given in English.

1. 회사(會社) _____

2. 회사원(會社員) _____

3. 회의(會議) _____

4. 회의실(會議室) _____

5. 회식(會食) _____

6. 회계(會計) _____

7. 회비(會費) _____

8. 회원(會員) _____

9. 회화(會話) _____

10. 사회(社會) _____

11. 국회(國會) _____

12. 대회(大會) _____

13. 교회(敎會) _____

14. 동호회(同好會) _____

Section II - Comprehension

Multiple choice. Circle the best answer.

15. What does 회(會) mean?

    a. house, residence   b. food, to eat

    c. gathering, to gather   d. room

16. Which of the following is unrelated to the others?

    a. 회의(會議)   b. 회식(會食)   c. 회화(會話)   d. 회사(會社)

17. Choose one word element that best fills in the blanks.

회(　　) 　(　　)산기 　(　　)산대 　회(　　)사

a. 의　　b. 계　　c. 원　　d. 화

18. In 교회(敎會), what does 교(敎) mean?

a. a college, a university
b. park
c. religion
d. to teach

19. Which of the following has the same meaning as 회의실(會議室)?

a. 교직원(敎職員)
b. 회의장(會議場)
c. 국회의원(國會議員)
d. 비용(費用)

Section III - Listening Comprehension

Listen to the dialogue and fill in the blanks with the missing word/phrase. The dialogue will be played twice.

A: 석진 씨, 회비 20. (　　　　　　　　)?

B: 아, 얼마죠?

A: 3만원이요.

B: 아, 지금 현금이 21. (　　　　　　　). 내일 22. (　　　　　　　).

Lesson 14.
Since, Because, As
-(으)니까

Section I - Vocabulary

Match each Korean word/phrase to its common English translation. All words and phrases are used in the following sections, so be sure to commit them to memory!

1. 어울리다   a. to be boring

2. 진하다   b. makeup

3. 필요하다   c. to suit

4. 지루하다   d. to clean (up)

5. 동네   e. to need

6. 청소하다   f. town, neighborhood

7. 이사   g. to be thick, to be heavy

8. 화장   h. move

Section II - Conjugation Practice

Complete the sentences by choosing the most appropriate word from the box + -(으)니까. Each word is used only once.

| 좋아하다 크다 좁다 없다 되다 하다 |

9. 10월 ~~~~~~~~~~ 확 추워졌어요.

10. 집이 ~~~~~~~~~~ 큰 침대는 못 사요.

11. 사람이 한 명도 ~~~~~~~~~~ 무서워요.

12. 화장을 진하게 ~~~~~~~~~~ 다른 사람 같아요.

13. 키가 ~~~~~~~~~~ 옷이 잘 어울리는 것 같아요.

14. 게임을 ~~~~~~~~~~ 좋은 컴퓨터가 필요한가 봐요.

Section III - Comprehension

Circle the correct phrase. If both answers are possible, underline both phrases.

15. 너무 (기뻐서) (기쁘니까) 울었어요.

16. (배고파서) (배고프니까) 빨리 밥 먹으러 가요.

17. (지루해서)(지루하니까) 그만 볼까요?

18. 비가 많이 (와서)(오니까) 옷이 다 젖었어요.

19. 사람들이 다 (나가서)(나갔으니까) 청소할까요?

20. 의사 선생님이 (친절해서)(친절하니까) 좋아요.

21. 이 동네가 너무 (시끄러워서)(시끄러우니까) 이사 갈 거예요.

22. 다른 학생들 (공부해서)(공부하니까) 조용히 하세요.

Section IV- Listening Comprehension

Listen to the sentences and fill in the blanks with the missing word/phrase. Each sentence will be played twice.

23. 지금 (   ) 나중에 전화해 주세요.

24. 오늘은 (   ) 우리 영화 내일 봐요.

25. (   ) 에어컨 켤까요?

Section I - Vocabulary

Review the vocabulary words from Talk To Me In Korean Level 5 Lesson 15 by translating them into English.

1. 이거 =

2. 저 =

3. 커피 =

4. 혹시 =

5. 감기 =

6. 어떤 =

7. 문제 =

Section II - Conjugation Practice

Circle the conjugation that goes with the word and translate it.

8. 누구+ -라도 / -이라도 =

9. 어디 + -라도 / -이라도 =

10. 언제 + -라도 / -이라도 =

11. 하루 + -라도 / -이라도 =

12. 잠시 + -라도 / -이라도 =

13. 한 명 + -라도 / -이라도 =

Section III - Fill in the Blank

Complete the sentences by choosing the most appropriate word from the box below + -(이)라도. Each word is used only once.

	과자	영화	이렇게	그거	뭐	사고

14. (   ) 마셔요. = Drink something at least.

15. (   ) 주세요. = At least give me that.

16. (   ) 났어요? = Did you get into an accident or what?

17. (   ) 먹을래요? = Would you like a snack at least?

18. (   ) 해야 돼요. = I should at least do this.

19. 내일 (   ) 볼래요? = Do you want to watch a movie or

something tomorrow?

Section IV - Listening Comprehension

Listen to the dialogue and answer the following questions. The dialogue will be played twice.

20. What is the weather like in the dialogue?

    a. It is snowing a lot.

    b. It just stopped snowing.

    c. It is raining a lot.

    d. It just stopped raining.

21. Choose the correct sentence according to the dialogue.

    a. The man is about to go out.

    b. The woman just came inside.

    c. The woman needs a towel.

    d. The man doesn't have a towel.

Section I - Vocabulary

Fill in the chart. The first one has been done for you.

Verb/Adjective	Meaning	Narrative Present Tense Form
1. 자다	to sleep	잔다
2. 굽다		
3. 팔다		
4. 예쁘다		
5. 있다		
6. 없다		
7. 좋다		
8. 지나가다		
9. 오다		
10. 초대하다		

Section II - Paraphrasing

The following sentences are in the plain present tense in 반말, or casual language. Rewrite them using -(ㄴ/는)다 so that they can express your surprise or excitement, or be directed at nobody in particular.

11. 오늘 날씨 좋아. ➤

12. 여기 강아지 있어. ➤

13. 저기 기차 지나가. ➤

14. 전화 와. ➤

The following sentences are in the plain future tense in 반말, or casual language. Rewrite them using -(ㄴ/는)다 so that the speaker implies that they want the listener to react.

15. 그럼 나는 여기서 기다릴게. ➤

16. 나 먼저 갈게. ➤

17. 다음에는 너 초대 안 할게. ➤

18. TV 안 볼 거지? 끌게. ➤

Section III - Reading Comprehension

Read the following narration script from a documentary film and answer the questions.

정국은 오늘도 아침 8시에 ㄱ.일어나다. 일어나서 제일 먼저 하는 일은 핸드폰을 보는 ㄴ.것이다. 메신저에 들어가서 문자를 확인하고 *SNS*에 밤새 친구들이 올린 사진들을 살펴본다. 마음에 드는 사진에는 '좋아요'를 누르기도 하고, 댓글을 남기기도 ㄷ.하다. 좋아하는 스포츠 팀의 경기 결과도 확인한다. 그렇게 약 한 시간 정도를 보낸 뒤에 이불 밖으로 ㄹ.나오다.

*SNS = Konglish expression for social media

19. Choose the correct conjugations of the underlined words.

    a. ㄱ.일어난다 - ㄴ.것인다 - ㄷ.하다 - ㄹ.나오다

    b. ㄱ.일어나다 - ㄴ.것이다 - ㄷ.하다 - ㄹ.나오다

    c. ㄱ.일어난다 - ㄴ.것이다 - ㄷ.한다 - ㄹ.나온다

    d. ㄱ.일어나다 - ㄴ.것인다 - ㄷ.한다 - ㄹ.나온다

20. Which of the following statements is INCORRECT according to the script?

    a. Jeong-guk usually gets up at 8AM.

    b. Jeong-guk likes sports.

    c. Jeong-guk looks at his phone as soon as he gets up.

    d. Jeong-guk usually spends an hour making his bed.

Section IV - Listening Comprehension

Listen to the sentences and fill in the blanks with the missing word/phrase. Each sentence will be played twice.

21. 어? 저기 내 친구들 (   )!

22. 전화가 안 돼요. 어? 다시 (   )!

23. 우와! 이거 (   )!

Lesson 17. 동사/형용사 + -(ㄴ/는)다고 (말하다)
(To say) that something/someone + verb/adjective

Section I - Vocabulary

Match each Korean word/phrase to its common English translation. All words and phrases are used in the following sections, so be sure to commit them to memory!

1. 외우다

2. 눈이 부시다

3. 떠나다

4. 고맙다

5. 이사

6. 소문

7. 소식

8. 축하하다

9. 결혼하다

10. 가사

a. lyrics

b. to congratulate

c. news

d. to memorize

e. to leave

f. rumor

g. to get married

h. to be thankful

i. to be blinded (by light)

j. move

Section II - Comprehension

Yesterday you met these people. Here are some of the things they said to you.

민수: 저 여름에 스페인으로 여행 가요.

경은: 저는 주로 도서관에서 공부해요.

진영: 가사 외우는 것이 힘들어요.

유진: 머리가 너무 길어서 더워요.

석훈: 선글라스를 안 쓰니까 눈이 부셔요.

지연: 저 내일 떠나요.

Later that day you tell another person what they said. Write the sentences using reported speech. The first one has been done for you.

11. 민수 씨가 여름에 스페인으로 여행 간다고 했어요.

12. 경은 씨가 _____.

13. 진영 씨가 _____.

14. 유진 씨가 _____.

15. 석훈 씨가 _____.

16. 지연 씨가 _____.

Section III - Contraction Practice

Shorten the underlined part of each sentence.

17. 비가 <u>온다고 하는</u> 이야기 ⤞

18. 축하<u>한다고 하는</u> 메시지 ⤞

19. 결혼<u>한다고 하는</u> 소식 ⤞

20. <u>춥다고 하는</u> 사람 ⤞

21. <u>재미있다고 하는</u> 소문 ⤞

22. <u>고맙다고 하는</u> 말 ⤞

Section IV - Listening Comprehension

Listen to the dialogue and fill in the blanks with the missing word/phrase. The dialogue will be played twice.

A: 석진 씨, 이사 23. (   ) 들었는데, 맞아요?

B: 네.

A: 언제 이사 가요?

B: 다음 달 15일에 이사 가요.

A: 아, 어디로 이사 24. (   ) 했죠?

B: 행복동으로 이사 가요.

A: 아, 그 동네 25. (   ) 소문 들었어요.

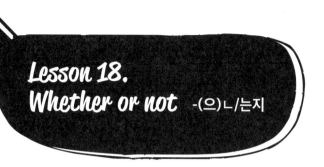

Lesson 18.
Whether or not -(으)ㄴ/는지

Section I - Vocabulary

Fill in the chart.

	Verb	Meaning	Verb + -(으)ㄴ/는지
1.	먹다		
2.	사다		
3.	놀다		
4.	풀다		
	Adjective	Meaning	Adjective + -(으)ㄴ/는지
5.	크다		
6.	예쁘다		
7.	작다		
8.	좁다		

Section II - Conjugation Practice

Combine the two sentences by using -(으)ㄴ/는지, then translate it into your preferred language (answers are provided in English only).

9. 이거 뭐예요? + 알아요?

10. 뭐가 좋아요? + 몰라요.

11. 문제가 있어요? + 물어보세요.

12. 이 사람 누구예요? + 알아요?

13. 이거 괜찮아요? + 봐 주세요.

14. 어떤 메뉴가 인기가 많아요? + 알려 주세요.

Section III - Comprehension

In the following sentences, the "or not" part of "whether or not" is left unsaid. Add "or not" to the following sentences.

15. 이 금이 진짜 금인지 ＿＿＿＿＿＿＿＿ 알고 싶어요.

16. 안에 사람이 있는지 ＿＿＿＿＿＿＿＿ 모르겠어요.

17. 답이 맞는지 ＿＿＿＿＿＿＿＿ 확인해 보세요.

18. 내일 우리 만날 수 있는지 ＿＿＿＿＿＿＿＿＿ 알고 싶어요.

19. 우리 숙소가 넓은지 ＿＿＿＿＿＿＿＿＿ 아직 몰라요.

숙소 = accommodation

Section IV - Listening Comprehension

Listen to the dialogue and answer the following questions. The dialogue will be played twice.

20. Choose the correct sentence according to the dialogue.

a. The man's computer broke.

b. The man fixed the computer.

c. The man was not able to fix the computer.

d. The man let the woman know how to fix the computer.

21. Which information is NOT given in the dialogue?

a. Who does the computer belong to.

b. Whether or not the computer has been fixed.

c. The man's name

d. The woman's name

Lesson 19. 동사 + -(으)라고 하다
To tell someone to do something

Section I - Vocabulary

Circle the correct translation of the Korean expression. Circle both if they are both correct. All words and phrases are used in the following sections, so be sure to commit them to memory!

1. 저쪽 길   a. this street/way   b. that street/way

2. 신발(을) 벗다   a. to put on shoes   b. to take off shoes

3. 피자(를) 시키다   a. to eat pizza   b. to order pizza

4. 조용히 하다   a. to make noise   b. to keep quiet

5. 피아노(를) 치다   a. to play the piano   b. to buy a piano

6. 뛰다   a. to jump   b. to run

7. 사진(을) 찍다   a. to take a picture   b. to post a picture

Section II - Conjugation Practice I

Quote the imperative statements. The first one has been done for you.

8. 민호: "저쪽 길로 가세요."

   나: "민호 씨가 저쪽 길로 가라고 했어요."

9. 수정: "신발 벗고 들어오세요."

   나: "＿＿＿＿＿＿＿＿＿＿＿＿＿＿＿＿＿＿."

10. 지은: "피자 시키세요."

   나: "＿＿＿＿＿＿＿＿＿＿＿＿＿＿＿＿＿＿."

11. 서현: "조용히 하세요."

   나: "＿＿＿＿＿＿＿＿＿＿＿＿＿＿＿＿＿＿."

12. 동욱: "너무 더우면 말하세요."

   나: "＿＿＿＿＿＿＿＿＿＿＿＿＿＿＿＿＿＿."

Section III - Conjugation Practice II

Quote the negative imperative statements. The first one has been done for you.

13. 경민: "걱정하지 마세요."

    나: "경민 씨가 걱정하지 말라고 했어요."

14. 윤지: "피아노 치지 마세요."

    나: "_____."

15. 정석: "불 켜지 마세요."

    나: "_____."

16. 진영: "뛰지 마세요."

    나: "_____."

17. 효린: "사진 찍지 마세요."

    나: "_____."

Section IV – Listening Comprehension

Listen to the dialogue and answer the following questions in Korean. The dialogue will be played twice.

18. Where did Hyunwoo tell the man to come?

19. By what time did Hyunwoo tell the man to come?

Lesson 20.
Sentence Building Drill #4

Section I - Vocabulary

Match each Korean word/phrase to its common English translation. All words and phrases are used in the following sections, so be sure to commit them to memory!

1. 말(을) 걸다   a. to return

2. 모기   b. event, function, ceremony

3. 반납하다   c. to initiate a conversation

4. 치우다   d. delivery

5. 행사   e. to get around, to go around

6. 길이 막히다   f. to bring (lit. to pack and bring)

7. 일이 생기다   g. to tidy up, to clean up

8. 싸 오다   h. to take a walk, to stroll

9. 돌아다니다   i. something comes up

10. 산책하다   j. video

11. 배달   k. mosquito

12. 사 오다   l. to buy (lit. to buy and bring)

13. 동영상   m. traffic is backed up
                       (lit. a road is blocked)

Section II - Conjugation Practice

The following exercises use all of the grammar points that you have learned so far. Complete the sentences using the grammar point and the words given in the parentheses. An example has been provided.

-(으)니까 -지 마세요. = …, so don't [verb].

> Example: (볼 거다, 끄다)
>
> TV <u>볼 거니까</u> <u>끄지 마세요.</u>

14. (바쁘다, 말 걸다)

  지금 ~~~~~~ .

15. (화장품이다, 먹다)

  이거 ~~~~~~ .

16. (들어오다, 열다)

  모기 ~~~~~~~~~~~~~~~~~~ 창문 ~~~~~~~~~~~~~~~~~~~~~~~ .

17. (쓸 거다, 반납하다)

  마이크 또 ~~~~~~~~~~~~~~~ 아직 ~~~~~~~~~~~~~~~~~~~~~~~~~ .

18. (늦을 거다, 기다리다)

~~~~~~~~~~~~~~~~~~~~~~~~~~~~~~~~~~~~~~ .

-(ㄴ/는)다고 하는데 -(으)ㄹ까요? = *[Someone] says that..., shall I/we [verb]?*

     Example: (오시다, 치우다)
     지금 손님 오신다고 하는데 좀 치울까요?

19. (비 오다, 취소하다)

   내일 ~~~~~~~~~~~~~~~~ 행사 ~~~~~~~~~~~~~~~~~~~~ ?

20. (막히다, 타고 가다)

   지금 길이 많이 ~~~~~~~~~~~~~~ 지하철 ~~~~~~~~~~~~~~~~~~ ?

21. (늦다, 출발하다)

   주연 씨가 ~~~~~~~~~~~~~ 저희 먼저 ~~~~~~~~~~~~~~~~~~ ?

22. (안 되다, 사 오다)

   전화해 보니까 배달이 ~~~~~~~~~~~~~ 제가 직접 가서 ~~~~~~~~~~~~~~~~~~ ?

23. (길다, 가다)

   지금 그 식당 앞에 줄이 ~~~~~~~~~~ 다른 식당으로 ~~~~~~~~~~~~~~ ?

-(으)려고 했는데, -아/어/여서 못 -았/었/였어요. = I was going to [verb], but...
so I/we couldn't [verb].

Example: (타다, 없다)
택시 타려고 했는데, 돈이 없어서 못 탔어요.

24. (만나다, 일이 생기다)

오늘 _____, 갑자기 _____.

25. (싸 오다, 일어나다)

도시락 _____, 늦게 _____.

26. (찍다, 없다)

동영상 _____, 폰 배터리가 _____.

27. (돌아다니다, 아프다)

더 _____, 다리가 너무 _____.

28. (산책하다, 들어가다)

오늘은 꼭 강아지랑 _____, 집에 너무

늦게 _____ 산책 _____.

Section III - Listening Comprehension

Listen to the sentence and fill in the blanks with the missing word/phrase. Each sentence will be played twice.

29. 지금 주연 씨가 바빠서 (   ), 저라도 갈까요?

30. 어제 친구랑 영화 보려고 했는데, (   ) 사람이

    너무 (   ) 영화를 못 봤어요.

31. 그거 비밀이니까 아직 아무한테도 (   ).

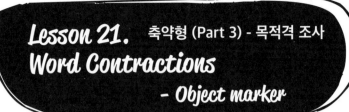
Section I - Vocabulary

Review the vocabulary words from Talk To Me In Korean Level 5 Lesson 21 by translating them into English.

1. 초대하다 =

2. 부르다 =

3. 누구 =

4. 기다리다 =

5. 누르다 =

6. 어떻게 =

7. 알려 주다 =

Section II - Contraction Practice

Circle the object markers and shorten the phrase if you can.

8. 너를 ⇾

9. 나를 ⇾

10. 겨울을 ⇾

11. 친구를 ⇾

12. 사랑을 ⇾

13. 선생님을 ⇾

14. 누구를 ⇾

Section III - Expansion Practice

Expand the underlined part of each sentence.

15. 절 초대해 주세요. ⇾

16. 여길 어떻게 알았어요? ⇾

17. 뭘 기다리고 있어요? ↣

18. 이걸 누구한테 줘야 돼요? ↣

19. 어딜 보고 있어요? ↣

Section IV - Listening Comprehension

Listen to the sentence and fill in the blanks with the missing word/phrase. Each sentence will be played twice.

20. 누가 (   ) 불렀어요?

21. (   ) 살 거예요?

22. (   ) 눌러야 돼요?

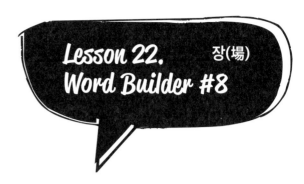

Section I - Vocabulary

Translate each word into English using what you know, Talk To Me In Korean Level 5 Lesson 22, or a dictionary, then define it in your preferred language (if not English). Translations in the Answer Key are given in English.

1. 음식(飮食) _____

2. 식당(食堂) _____

3. 음식점(飮食店) _____

4. 식사(食事) _____

5. 식탁(食卓) _____

6. 식품(食品) _____

7. 간식(間食) _____

8. 후식(後食) _____

9. 과식(過食) _____

10. 시식(試食) _____

11. 분식(粉食) _____

12. 외식(外食) _____

Section II - Comprehension

Multiple choice. Circle the best answer.

13. What does 식(食) mean?

    a. place, venue

    b. thing, item

    c. outside, exterior

    d. food, to eat

14. Which of the following does NOT refer to food?

    a. 식당

    b. 식품

    c. 음식

    d. 후식

15. In 간식(間食), what does 간(間) mean?

    a. drink

    b. powder, flour

    c. gap, space

    d. back, after

16. Choose the word that best completes the sentence.

어제 (   )한 것 같아요. = I think I ate too much yesterday.

a. 미식   b. 시식

c. 치식   d. 과식

17. Choose one word element that best fills in the blanks.

식(   ) = (dining) table
(   )자 = table
(   )구 = table tennis

a. 사(事)   b. 점(店)

c. 음(飮)   d. 탁(卓)

Section III - Listening Comprehension

Listen to the dialogue and fill in the blanks with the missing word/phrase. The dialogue will be played twice.

A: 경화 씨, 방금 전에 18. (   ), 또 간식 먹어요?

B: 네. 드실래요?

A: 아니요. 19. (   ). 저는 배불러요.

Lesson 23.
It seems like ...,
I assume ...
-(으)려나 보다

Section I - Vocabulary

Match each Korean word/phrase to its common English translation. All words and phrases are used in the following sections, so be sure to commit them to memory!

1. 예쁘다

2. 걸어가다

3. 깨끗하다

4. 춥다

5. 덥다

6. 눕다

7. 듣다

8. 부르다

9. 짓다

10. 바닥

11. 몰래

a. to lie down

b. to be hot

c. to call (out)

d. to walk

e. to build

f. secretly

g. to be clean

h. to be pretty

i. floor

j. to hear, to listen

k. to be cold

Section II - Comprehension

Multiple Choice. Circle the best answer.

12. Choose the most unnatural sentence.

    a. 예쁘려나 봐요

    b. 걸어가려나 봐요

    c. 깨끗해지려나 봐요

    d. 추우려나 봐요

13. The following statements compare -(으)려나 보다 and -(으)ㄹ 것 같다.
    Which statement is INCORRECT?

    a. -(으)려나 보다 is more of a deduction about something.

    b. -(으)ㄹ 것 같다 is more of a hunch about something.

    c. You sound more certain of your statement when using -(으)려나 보다.

    d. -(으)려나 보다 is used when making a statement based on what you saw.

14. Which statement is INCORRECT?

    a. -(으)려나 보다 is a shortened form of -(으)려고 하나 보다.

    b. -(으)려나 보다 is a way of expressing your assumption about a past action.

    c. When a verb stem ends with a vowel, you attach -려나 보다.

    d. When a verb stem ends with a consonant, you attach -으려나 보다.

15. Which of the followings sounds the most unnatural?

    a. 더우려나 봐요   *b.* 더워지려나 봐요

    c. 깨끗하려나 봐요   *d.* All of the above sound unnatural

16. Which of the following conjugations is correct?

    a. 바닥에 눕다 + -(으)려나 보다 = 바닥에 눕으려나 보다

    b. 몰래 듣다 + -(으)려나 보다 = 몰래 듣으려나 보다

    c. 사람을 부르다 + -(으)려나 보다 = 사람을 부르려나 보다

    d. 집을 짓다 + -(으)려나 보다 = 집을 짓으려나 보다

Section III - Paraphrasing

Change the sentence conjugation from -(으)려고 하다 to -(으)려나 보다 to express an assumption.

    Ex) 아기가 울려고 해요. ➤ 아기가 울려나 봐요.

    (The baby is about to cry. ➤ It looks like the baby is about to cry.)

17. 지금 시작하려고 해요. ➤

18. 다 같이 들어오려고 해요. ➤

19. 카페 문을 닫으려고 해요. ➤

20. 중국 음식 시키려고 해요. ➤

21. 공부를 열심히 하려고 해요. ➤

22. 가족하고 여행을 가려고 해요. ➤

Section IV - Listening Comprehension

Listen to the dialogue and answer the following questions. The dialogue will be played twice.

23. Did Soo-yeong bring his lunch?

    a. Yes   b. No

24. Did Hyunwoo order his lunch?

    a. Yes. He ordered his lunch.

    b. No. He didn't order his lunch yet.

Lesson 24.
Not A but B, Don't do THIS but do THAT

말고, -지 말고

Section I - Vocabulary

Match each Korean word/phrase to its common English translation. All words and phrases are used in the following sections, so be sure to commit them to memory!

1. 숨기다   a. there

2. 얘기하다   b. another song, a different song

3. 미루다   c. to hide

4. 미리미리   d. chocolate

5. 여기   e. tea

6. 거기   f. to tell, to talk

7. 차   g. here

8. 다른 노래   h. candy

9. 사탕   i. in advance, ahead

10. 초콜릿   j. to put off

Talk To Me In Korean Workbook

Section II - Translation Practice

Translate the phrases into Korean using 말고.

11. not coffee, but tea =

12. not this one, but that one over there =

13. not cold water, but hot water =

14. not this song, but another song =

15. not candy, but chocolate =

16. not there, but here =

Section III - Conjugation Practice

Combine the two sentences that are given by using -지 말고.

17. 그쪽으로 가지 마세요. 이쪽으로 오세요. ⤳

18. 저 기다리지 마세요. 먼저 가세요. ⤳

19. 지금 사지 마세요. 조금만 기다리세요. ⤳

20. 늦지 마세요. 일찍 오세요. ↣

21. 숨기지 마세요. 얘기하세요. ↣

22. 미루지 마세요. 미리미리 하세요. ↣

23. 걱정하지 마세요. 그냥 해 보세요. ↣

Section IV - Listening Comprehension

Listen to the dialogue and answer the following question. The dialogue will be played twice.

24. What would Kyung-hwa like to have according to the dialogue? Write the answer in Korean.

(   )

Listen to another dialogue and answer the following question. The dialogue will be played twice.

25. Choose the correct sentence according to the dialogue.

    a. Kyeong-eun told Jooyeon not to eat and wait for her.
    b. Kyeong-eun told Jooyeon not to wait and eat first.
    c. Jooyeon told Kyeong-eun not to eat and wait for her.
    d. Jooyeon told Kyeong-eun not to wait and eat first.

Lesson 25.
Compared to, Relatively
-에 비해서 -(으)ㄴ/는 편이다

Section I - Vocabulary

Fill in the chart.

Word/Expression in Infinitive Form	Meaning	Present Tense	+ -(으)ㄴ/는 편이에요
1. 작다			
2. 쉽다			
3. 크다			
4. 바쁘다			
5. 비싸다			
6. 빠르다			
7. 잘하다			
8. 조용하다			
9. 피아노를 잘 치다			
10. 자주 오다			

Section II - Comprehension

Rewrite the following sentences that are directly comparing two things to a less direct and softer sentence by using -에 비해서 -(으)ㄴ/는 편이다. An example has been provided.

Ex) 버스보다 지하철이 빨라요. ➝ 버스에 비해서 지하철이 빠른 편이에요.
(The subway is faster than the bus. ➝ Compared to the bus, the subway is pretty fast.)

11. 이 길보다 저 길이 안 막혀요.

➝

12. 다른 가게보다 이 가게가 싸요.

➝

13. 수학은 저보다 석진이가 잘해요.

➝

14. 저는 드라마보다 영화를 많이 봐요.

➝

15. 빨간색 구두보다 검은색 구두가 잘 팔려요.

➝

16. 다른 브랜드 옷보다 이 브랜드 옷이 예뻐요.

 →

 **Section III - Listening Comprehension**

Listen to the dialogue and fill in the blanks with the missing word/phrase. The dialogue will be played twice.

A: 로빈 씨 가족은 다 키가 17. (   ).

B: 그래요? 그렇게 18. (   ) 아니라고 생각했는데.

A: 저희 가족에 비하면 19. (   ).

Lesson 26.
Instead of, In return
대신에, -는 대신에

Section I - Vocabulary

Match each Korean word/phrase to its common English translation. All words and phrases are used in the following sections, so be sure to commit them to memory!

1. 꿩   a. cooked rice, steamed rice

2. 문자   b. to dye (one's hair), to color (one's hair)

3. 포기하다   c. chicken

4. 머릿결   d. to arrive

5. 빵   e. pheasant

6. 염색하다   f. text message

7. 사탕   g. proverb

8. 닭   h. quality/state of one's hair

9. 속담   i. bread

10. 퇴근하다   j. to give up

11. 밥   k. candy

12. 도착하다   l. to get off (of work)

100   **Talk To Me In Korean Workbook**

Section II - Comprehension

The 에 in 대신에 is often dropped in everyday conversation. Translate the following phrases into Korean using 대신 and then write the most appropriate phrase in the dialogue below.

13. chicken instead of pheasant

    =

14. bread instead of (cooked) rice

    =

15. a text message instead of a phone call

    =

16. a camera instead of a computer

    =

17. candy instead of chocolate

    =

18. A: 집에 도착하면 전화할게요.

    B: _____ 주세요.

19. A: 아침에 밥 먹었어요?

    B: _____ 먹었어요.

20. A: 밸런타인데이에 초콜릿 받았어요?

    B: ＿＿＿＿＿＿＿＿＿＿ 받았어요.

21. A: 한국에는 ＿＿＿＿＿＿＿＿＿＿ 이라는 속담이 있어요. 알아요?

    B: 아니요. 몰라요.

22. A: 컴퓨터 샀어요?

    B: 아니요. ＿＿＿＿＿＿＿＿＿＿ 샀어요.

Section III - Conjugation Practice

Complete the sentences below by choosing a word from each box and conjugating it with -는 대신에 -아/어/여야 되다. Each word is used only once. Choose either polite or casual form, depending on the context.

-는 대신에

| 놀다 | 예뻐지다 | 빌려주다 | 사다 | 가다 |

-아/어/여야 되다

| 먹다 | 오다 | 공부하다 | 포기하다 | 도와주다 |

23.

    A: 경화 씨, 벌써 퇴근해요?

    B: 네. 하지만 오늘 일찍 _____, 내일 일찍 _____.

24.

    A: 이것 좀 빌려줄 수 있어요?

    B: 제가 이거 _____, 저 영어 공부 _____.

25.

    A: 엄마, 밖에 나가서 친구들이랑 놀아도 돼요?

    B: 흠… 그럼 지금 _____, 이따가 _____. 알겠지?

26.

    A: 오늘 밥은 네가 사.

    B: 좋아. 그런데 내가 _____, 내가 먹고 싶은 것 _____. 괜찮지?

27.

    A: 제 머리 이 색으로 염색하면 어떨까요?

    B: 예쁠 것 같아요. 근데 _____, 머릿결은 _____.

Section IV - Listening Comprehension

Listen to the dialogue and answer the following questions. The dialogue will be played twice.

28. Which of the following statements is true?

    a. Seokjin often calls Minjeong.

    b. Minjeong called Seokjin instead of texting him.

    c. Minjeong was supposed to call Seokjin, but she didn't.

    d. Minjeong was supposed to text Seokjin, but she didn't.

29. What is the woman going to do right after this dialogue?

    a. She will go home.

    b. She will call Seokjin.

    c. She will text Seokjin.

    d. She will wake Seokjin up.

Lesson 27.
You know, Isn't it ...?, You see ..., Come on ...
-잖아(요)

Section I - Vocabulary

Match each Korean word/phrase to its common English translation. All words and phrases are used in the following sections, so be sure to commit them to memory!

1. 캐릭터

2. 인기가 많다

3. 이렇게

4. 빵집

5. 중국집

6. 영상

7. 소리

8. 녹음

9. 예전

10. 바뀌다

a. video

b. like this, this

c. to be changed

d. recording

e. sound

f. character

g. to be popular

h. old

i. bakery

j. Chinese restaurant

Section II - Conjugation Practice

Change the endings of the following sentences to –잖아요.

11. 있어요. ↣

12. 있었어요. ↣

13. 알아요. ↣

14. 알았어요. ↣

15. 추워요. ↣

16. 추웠어요. ↣

17. 말해요. ↣

18. 말했어요. ↣

19. 귀여워요. ↣

20. 귀여웠어요. ↣

21. 재밌어요. ↦

22. 재밌었어요. ↦

23. 일요일이에요. ↦

24. 일요일이었어요. ↦

Section III - Fill in the Blank

Complete the dialogues by using the conjugated phrases from Section II - Conjugation Practice. Each expression is used only once.

25.

    A: 우리가 한국에 언제 갔죠?

    B: 그때 엄청 _____ . 겨울에 갔죠.

26.

    A: 이 캐릭터는 왜 이렇게 인기가 많을까요?

    B: _____ . 안 귀여워요?

27.

    A: 어? 왜 빵집이 문을 닫았죠?

    B: 오늘 _____ .

28.

    A: 이 영상 다시 찍어야 돼요.

    B: 왜요?

    A: 제가 아까 _____. 소리가 녹음이 안 됐어요.

29.

    A: 저희 예전 사무실 앞에 큰 중국집 _____. 지금은 카페로
    바뀌었어요.

    B: 아, 정말요?

Section IV - Comprehension

Rewrite the dialogues from Section III - Fill in the Blank in 반말 (casual language).

25a.

26a.

27a.

28a.

29a.

                    Talk To Me In Korean Workbook

Section V – Listening Comprehension
Listen to the dialogue and fill in the blanks with the missing word/phrase. The dialogue will be played twice.

A: 다 30. (   )?

B: 수연이는?

A: 수연이는 31. (   ). 안 불렀어.

B: 그래도 전화 한번 해 보자.

Lesson 28. -(으)ㄹ 수밖에 없다
To have no other choice but to ...

Section I - Vocabulary

Match each Korean word/phrase to its common English translation. All words and phrases are used in the following sections, so be sure to commit them to memory!

1.	축구 선수	a. necklace
2.	무릎	b. all day
3.	밝다	c. to be bright
4.	친절하다	d. children
5.	저렴하다	e. to be kind
6.	부상	f. knee
7.	목걸이	g. to get hurt, to be injured
8.	아이들	h. to be serious, to be severe
9.	하루 종일	i. injury
10.	다치다	j. inexpensive
11.	심각하다	k. soccer player

Section II - Conjugation Practice

Conjugate the verb or adjective with -(으)ㄹ 수밖에 없다.

12. 사다 + -(으)ㄹ 수밖에 없다 =

13. 포기하다 + -(으)ㄹ 수밖에 없다 =

14. 좋아하다 + -(으)ㄹ 수밖에 없다 =

15. 어렵다 + -(으)ㄹ 수밖에 없다 =

16. 비싸다 + -(으)ㄹ 수밖에 없다 =

17. 시끄럽다 + -(으)ㄹ 수밖에 없다 =

Section III - Comprehension

Complete the dialogues by conjugating the expressions from Section II - Conjugation Practice in the correct tense. Each expression is used only once.

18.

A: 이 목걸이는 정말 비싸네요.

B: _____. 이게 다 다이아몬드예요.

19.

A: 가방 새로 샀어요?

B: _____. 너무 예쁜데 가격도 저렴했어요.

20.

    A: 경화 씨, 재민 씨 좋아해요?

    B: 당연하죠. 재민 씨는 항상 밝고 친절해서 ~~~~~~~~~~~~~~~~~~~~~.

21.

    A: 저는 어릴 때 축구 선수였는데 무릎을 다쳐서 축구를 ~~~~~~~~~~~~~~~.

    B: 심각한 부상이었나 봐요.

22.

    A: 이 글은 너무 어려워요.

    B: 이건 뉴스 기사여서 ~~~~~~~~~~~~~~~~.

23.

    A: 이 집에는 아이들이 굉장히 많네요.

    B: 네. 그래서 하루 종일 ~~~~~~~~~~~~~~~~~~~~.

Section IV - Paraphrasing

Replace -(으)ㄹ 수밖에 없어요 with 안 -(으)ㄹ 수가 없어요, which means the same thing.

24. 어제 밤늦게까지 공부를 해서, 오늘 피곤할 수밖에 없어요.

    →

25. 미안하지만 이렇게 할 수밖에 없어요.

　　↠

26. 그럴 수밖에 없어요.

　　↠

27. 또 이야기할 수밖에 없어요.

　　↠

28. 걱정이 될 수밖에 없어요.

　　↠

Section V - Listening Comprehension

Listen to the dialogue and fill in the blanks with the missing word/phrase. The dialogue will be played twice.

A: 나 태환이랑 수영 시합했는데 졌어.

B: 네가 29. (　　　　　　　　　　　　　　　).

　　태환이는 30. (　　　　　　　　　　　　　).

A: 그래도 평영은 자신 있었는데…

Lesson 29. -았/었/였다고, -(으)ㄹ 거라고
They said that they had done ...,
They said that they would ...

Section I - Vocabulary

Match each Korean word/phrase to its common English translation. All words and phrases are used in the following sections, so be sure to commit them to memory!

1. 감기에 걸리다   a. to quit

2. 고치다   b. when

3. 괜찮다   c. to go back, to return

4. 고장 나다   d. to fix, to repair

5. 그만두다   e. to not be hungry

6. 돌아가다   f. to catch a cold

7. 최근에   g. to be okay, to be fine

8. 언제   h. to break, to be broken

9. 배 안 고프다   i. recently

Section II - Conjugation Practice

Quote what your friend said to you yesterday to another friend that you met today, like the example provided.

Yesterday   Today

Ex) 지원 씨가 도와줄 거라고 했어요.

지원 제가 도와줄게요. Me

슬기

10. ～～～～～～～～～～～
～～～～～～～～～～～

민기 생일 파티를 할 거예요. Me

지연

11. ～～～～～～～～～～
～～～～～～～～～～

용호 다음에 다시 올게요. Me

태민

12. ～～～～～～～～～～
～～～～～～～～～～

석원 내일 비 올 거예요. Me

주은

Section III - Fill in the Blank

Complete the sentences by quoting what you heard earlier today.

Earlier Today   Now

민호 씨가 감기에 걸렸어요.

Me

16. 민호 씨, ~~~~~~ 들었는데, 괜찮아요?

민호

석진 씨 사무실 컴퓨터가 고장 났어요.

Me

17. 석진 씨, ~~~~~~ 들었는데, 고쳤어요?

석진

주연 씨가 오늘 학교에 안 갔어요.

Me

18. 주연 씨, ~~~~~~ 들었는데, 무슨 일 있어요?

주연

지민 씨 회사 그만둘 거예요.

Me

19. 지민 씨, ~~~~~~ 들었는데, 맞아요?

지민

Earlier Today

Now

에밀리 씨 미국으로 돌아갈 거예요.

Me

20. 에밀리 씨, ＿＿＿＿＿＿
들었는데, 언제 가요?

에밀리

경화 씨는 밥 안 먹을 거예요.

Me

21. 경화 씨, ＿＿＿＿＿
들었는데, 배 안 고파요?

경화

Section IV - Listening Comprehension

Listen to the dialogue and fill in the blanks with the missing word/phrase. The dialogue will be played twice.

A: 주연 씨 휴가 언제 22. (   )?

B: 4월에요.

A: 어디로 23. (   )?

B: 베트남이요. 하노이 갈 거예요.

Talk To Me In Korean Workbook

Lesson 30.
Sentence Building Drill #5

Section I - Vocabulary

Match each Korean word/phrase to its common English translation. All words and phrases are used in the following sections, so be sure to commit them to memory!

1.	부탁	a.	next time
2.	오래	b.	to stay
3.	혼자	c.	instead of
4.	뜨다	d.	favor, request
5.	시키다	e.	to help
6.	머물다 (short for 머무르다)	f.	alone, by oneself
7.	도와주다	g.	to order
8.	다음번에	h.	to rise, to come out, to come up
9.	런치 메뉴	i.	long, (for) a long time
10.	(-는) 대신에	j.	lunch menu

Section II - Matching

Take a sentence fragment from column A, match it with the most appropriate fragment from column B, and write it as one sentence on the line below.

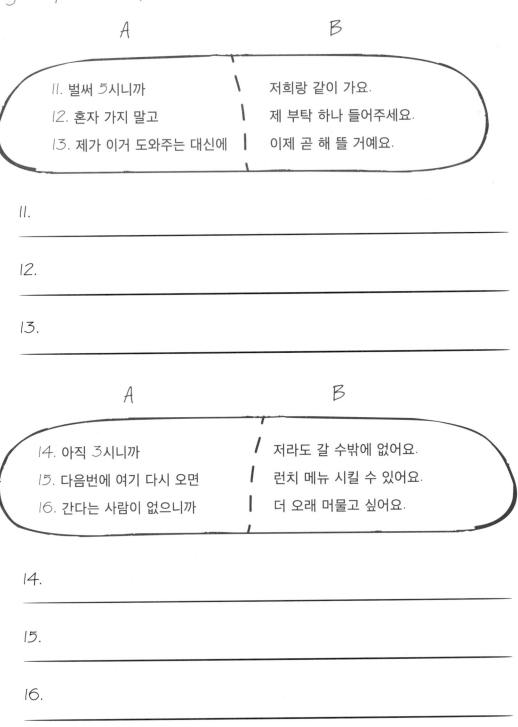

A

B

11. 벌써 5시니까

12. 혼자 가지 말고

13. 제가 이거 도와주는 대신에

저희랑 같이 가요.

제 부탁 하나 들어주세요.

이제 곧 해 뜰 거예요.

11.

_____

12.

_____

13.

_____

A

B

14. 아직 3시니까

15. 다음번에 여기 다시 오면

16. 간다는 사람이 없으니까

저라도 갈 수밖에 없어요.

런치 메뉴 시킬 수 있어요.

더 오래 머물고 싶어요.

14.

_____

15.

_____

16.

_____

Talk To Me In Korean Workbook

Section III - Listening Comprehension

Listen to the sentence and fill in the blank with the missing word/phrase. Each sentence will be played twice.

17. 벌써 (   ), 오늘 가지 말고 내일 가요.

18. 제가 이거 도와주는 대신에, 다음번에 제가 (   ) 들어줘야 돼요.

19. 지금은 다른 (   ) 저라도 갈 수밖에 없어요.

Answer Key
for
TTMIK
Workbook
Level 5

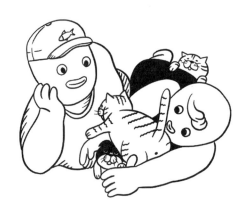

Lesson 1

Section I - Vocabulary

1. e
2. a
3. f
4. c
5. h
6. b
7. g
8. d

Section II - Translation Practice

9. 죽을 뻔했어요.
10. 울 뻔했어요.
11. 말할 뻔했어요.
12. 들킬 뻔했어요. or 잡힐 뻔했어요.
13. 차에 치일 뻔했어요.
14. 의자에서 떨어질 뻔했어요.
15. 기차를 놓칠 뻔했어요.
16. 사고(가) 날 뻔했어요.
9a. 하마터면 죽을 뻔했어요.
10a. 하마터면 울 뻔했어요.
11a. 하마터면 말할 뻔했어요.
12a. 하마터면 들킬 뻔했어요. or 하마터면 잡힐 뻔했어요.
13a. 하마터면 차에 치일 뻔했어요.
14a. 하마터면 의자에서 떨어질 뻔했어요.
15a. 하마터면 기차를 놓칠 뻔했어요.
16a. 하마터면 사고(가) 날 뻔했어요.

Section III - Listening Comprehension

A: 아! 정말 아쉬워요. (= Ugh! That was a shame.)

B: 왜요? (= What happened?)

A: 달리기 일 등 할 17.뻔했는데, 넘어져서 오 등 했어요. (= I almost came in first, but I tripped, so I came in fifth.)

B: 진짜요? 저는 18.넘어질 뻔했는데, 안 넘어 졌어요. (= Really? I almost tripped, but I didn't.)

Lesson 2

Section I - Comprehension

1. -시-
2. 님
3. -께서
4. -세요
5. d. 이거 보실 거예요?

Section II - Conjugation Practice

6. 먹어도 ⇨ 드셔도
7. 좋아해서 ⇨ 좋아하셔서
8. 들어와요. ⇨ 들어오세요.
9. 어디 가요? ⇨ 어디 가세요?
10. 물 마실래요? ⇨ 물 드실래요?
11. 선생님 왔어요. ⇨ 선생님 오셨어요.
12. 지금 보면 안 돼요. ⇨ 지금 보시면 안 돼요.
13. 이 책상 팔 거예요? ⇨ 이 책상 파실 거예요?

Section III - Listening Comprehension

A: 안녕하세요. (= Hello.)

B: 안녕하세요. 사장님 어디 14.가셨어요? (= Hello. Where is your boss?)

A: 손님 15. 오셔서 잠깐 16. 나가셨어요. (= A guest came by, so he went out for a moment with him/her.)

Lesson 3

Section I - Comprehension

1. c

2. d

3. b

4. d

5. d

Section II - Listening Comprehension

(Creak)

여: 어? 녹음 다 하셨어요? = Oh, you finished recording?

남: 응. 다 했어. = Yeah, I'm finished.

여: 아, 수고하셨습니다. = Ah, congratulations on finishing it.

남: 너도 녹음할 거 있어? = Do you also have something to record?

여: 네. = Yes.

남: 그래. 수고해. = I see. Bye then.

6. Man

7. b

Lesson 4

Section I - Vocabulary

1. 집에서 공부하다 = to study at home

2. 주연 씨랑 경화 씨랑 만나다 = Jooyeon and Kyung-hwa meet

3. 친하게 지내다 = to stay close to (someone)

4. 빨리 걷다 = to walk quickly

5. 과자를 좋아하다 = to like snacks

6. 부모님이랑 살다 = to live with one's parents

7. 아무도 없다 = there is no one/nobody

8. 비가 오다 = to rain

Section II - Tense Conjugation

1a.

[Present tense] >> 경은 씨는 주로 집에서 공부하나 봐요. = I guess Kyeong-eun usually studies at home.

[Past tense] >> 주말에 집에서 열심히 공부했나 봐요. = I guess you studied hard at home over the weekend.

2a.

[Present tense] >> 주연 씨랑 경화 씨랑 자주 만나나 봐요. = I guess Jooyeon and Kyung-hwa often meet.

[Past tense] >> 주연 씨랑 경화 씨랑 어제 만났나 봐요. = I guess Jooyeon and Kyung-hwa met yesterday.

3a.

[Present tense] >> 우진이가 학교에서 친구들이랑 친하게 지내나 봐요. = I guess Woojin stays close to his friends at school.

[Past tense] >> 우진이가 종현이랑 제일 친하게 지냈나 봐요. = I guess Woojin stayed closest to Jong-hyun.

4a.

[Present tense] >> 제가 너무 빨리 걷나 봐요. = I guess I walk too fast.

[Past tense] >> 제가 너무 빨리 걸었나 봐요. = I guess I walked too fast.

5a.

[Present tense] >> 현우 씨는 과자를 좋아하나 봐요. = I guess Hyunwoo likes snacks.

[Past tense] >> 어렸을 때 과자를 좋아했나 봐요. = I guess you liked snacks when you were young.

6a.

[Present tense] >> 석진 씨는 아직도 부모님이랑 사나 봐요. = I guess Seokjin still lives with his parents.

[Past tense] >> 그때는 부모님이랑 살았나 봐요. = I guess you lived with your parents back then.

7a.

[Present tense] >> (똑똑) 저기요! 여기 아무도 없나 봐요. = (Knock knock) Hello? I guess there is no one here.

[Past tense] >> 택배 왔을 때 집에 아무도 없었나 봐요. = When the delivery came, I guess there was nobody at home.

8a.

[Present tense] >> 지금 밖에 비가 많이 오나 봐요. = I guess it is raining a lot outside at the moment.

[Past tense] >> 새벽에 비가 왔나 봐요. = I guess it rained at dawn.

Section III - Listening Comprehension

A: 저기 무슨 행사 9.하나 봐요. 사람들이 많이 모여 있어요. (= It looks like some event is going on over there. There are many people gathered there.)

B: 한번 가 볼까요? (= Shall we go and see it?)

A: 아! 다 10.끝났나 봐요. (= Oh, it seems like it is all over now.)

Lesson 5

Section I - Vocabulary

1. 똑똑하다: adjective / to be smart, to be clever

2. 잘하다: verb / to do something well, to be good at something, to do something often, to be kind to someone

3. 궁금하다: adjective / to be curious

4. 어색하다: adjective / to be awkward

5. 기대하다: verb / to look forward to, to anticipate, to expect

6. 힘들다: adjective / to be hard, to be difficult, to be tough

7. 여동생: noun / younger sister

8. 초인종: noun / doorbell

9. 누르다: verb / to press, to push

10. 답: noun / answer, reply

Section II - Grammar Point Comprehension

11. b (Verbs are followed by -나 보다.)

12. c (Even though the rule is that adjectives are followed by -(으)ㄴ가 보다, Korean speakers often use -나 보다 with adjectives when the stem ends with a consonant.)

13. d (Adjectives are followed by -(으)ㄴ가 보다.)

14. c (Verbs are followed by -나 보다, so 기대하나 봐요 is correct.)

15. d (-(은)가 보다 and -나 보다 are normally used when you are talking about someone other than yourself.)

Section III - Conjugation Practice

16. 하고 싶은가 봐요. = I guess he/she wants to do (it).

17. 하고 있나 봐요. = I guess he/she is doing (it).

18. 하지 않나 봐요. = I guess he/she doesn't do (it).

*When -지 않다 is attached to an adjective, -지 않은가 봐요 is correct.

19. 하게 되나 봐요. = I guess he/she gets to do (it). or I guess he/she ends up doing (it).

20. 할 수 없나 봐요. = I guess he/she cannot do (it).

21. 해야 하나 봐요. = I guess he/she has to do (it).

22. 해도 되나 봐요. = I guess it is okay to do (it).

23. 하면 안 되나 봐요. = I guess you shouldn't do (it).

Section IV - Listening Comprehension

A: 석진 씨가 24. 집에 없나 봐요. (= I guess Seokjin is not at home.)

B: 왜요? 답이 없어요? (= Why? There's no answer?)

A: 네. 초인종을 여러 번 눌렀는데 아무도 안 나와요. (= Yes. I rang the doorbell several times, but nobody came out.)

B: 분명히 집에 있는데… 아마 25. 자고 있나 봐요. (= I'm quite certain that he is home. I guess he is probably sleeping.)

Lesson 6

Section I - Vocabulary, Part 1

1. 문화(文化): culture

2. 문서(文書): document, papers

3. 문장(文章): sentence

4. 문자(文字): letter, character

5. 문학(文學): literature

6. 문법(文法): grammar

7. 주문(注文): order

8. 논문(論文): thesis, research paper

9. 문화재(文化財): cultural assets, cultural properties

Section II - Vocabulary, Part 2

10. 인간문화재 = human cultural assets

11. 영국 문학 = English literature

12. 고대 문자 = ancient character/letter

13. 주문 번호 = order number

14. 한국어 문장 = Korean sentence

15. 한국 문화 = Korean culture

16. 새 문서 = new document

17. 논문 제출했어요? = Have you submitted your thesis?

18. 문법 공부하는 거 싫어해요. = I hate studying grammar.

Section III - Listening Comprehension

A: 오늘 주문 19. 들어온 거 있어요? (= Were there any orders placed today?)

B: 아직 없어요. (= Nothing yet.)

A: 주문 20. 들어오면 문서에 21. 기록해 주세요. (= If an order comes in, please write it on the document.)

B: 네. (= I will.)

Lesson 7

Section I - Vocabulary

1. to fall asleep

2. work

3. to start

4. to make a phone call

5. to like

6. again

7. to come out

Section II - Conjugation Practice

8. 도착하자마자 전화할게요. = I will call you as soon as I arrive.

9. 가자마자 전화를 했어요. = As soon as I went there, I made a phone call.

10. 들어가자마자 다시 나왔어요. = As soon as I went in, I came right back out.

11. 보자마자 마음에 들었어요. = As soon as I saw it, I liked it.

12. 집에 오자마자 잠들었어요. = I fell asleep as soon as I came home.

13. 졸업하자마자 일을 시작할 거예요. = I will start working as soon as I graduate.

Section III - Listening Comprehension

A: 은지 씨, 은지 씨는 회사에 14. 출근하자마자 바로 일 시작해요? (= Eun-ji, do you start working right away as soon as you get to the office?)

B: 네. 대신 퇴근 시간 15. 되자마자 퇴근해요. (= Yes. I go home as soon as office hours are over instead.)

Lesson 8

Section I - Vocabulary

1. c

2. f

3. d

4. g

5. i

6. h

7. e

8. b

9. j

10. a

Section II - Comprehension

11. T

12. S

13. S

14. T

15. T

16. S

Section III - Conjugation Practice

[Present tense]

17. 지금 출발하려고 하는데, 석진 씨가 아직 안 왔어요.

= We are about to leave now, but Seokjin hasn't come yet.

18. TOPIK 시험을 보려고 하는데, 혼자 공부해도 될까요?

= I am planning to take the TOPIK exam, I wonder if it is okay to study by myself.

19. 카메라 사려고 하는데, 뭐가 좋아요?

= I am planning to buy a camera. Which one is good?

[Past tense]

20. 어제 친구 만나려고 했는데, 못 만났어요.

= I was going to meet a friend yesterday, but I couldn't meet her.

21. 참으려고 했는데 너무 배고파서 먼저 먹었

어요.

= I was going to resist, but I ate it first because I was too hungry.

22. 친구들이랑 축구 하려고 했는데 비가 와서 취소됐어요.

= I was going to play soccer with my friends, but it got canceled because it rained.

Section IV - Fill in the Blank

23. 이사하려고 하는 친구 = a friend who is planning to move (움직이려고 하는 친구 is also possible)

24. 외국에서 공부하려고 하는 학생들 = students who are planning to study abroad

25. 공을 잡으려고 하는 선수 = a player who is about to catch a ball (공을 받으려고 하는 선수 is also possible)

26. 밥을 먹으려고 하는 사람 = a person who is going to have a meal / a person who is about to have a meal

27. 가방을 사려고 하는 손님 = a customer who is planning to buy a bag / a customer who is about to buy a bag

Section V - Listening Comprehension

A: 왜 방문을 닫아 놨어요? (= Why have you shut the door?)

B: 강아지가 자꾸 28. 들어가려고 해서요. (= Because my dog keeps trying to go inside.)

A: 그래도 막 29. 열려고 하지 않아요? (= Doesn't he still try to open it?)

Lesson 9

Section I - Vocabulary

1. c
2. d
3. g
4. h
5. a
6. b
7. j
8. f
9. e
10. i

Section II - Writing Practice

11. 서울에서 살고 있었어요. 제주도로 이사 갔어요.

⇨ 서울에서 살다가 제주도로 이사 갔어요. (= I was living in Seoul, and then I moved to Jeju Island.)

12. 밥 먹고 있었어요. 전화를 받았어요.

⇨ 밥 먹다가 전화를 받았어요. (= I was eating and then I received a phone call.)

13. 집에서 공부하고 있었어요. 나왔어요.

⇨ 집에서 공부하다가 나왔어요. (= I was studying at home and then came outside.)

14. 텔레비전을 보고 있었어요. 잠이 들었어요.

⇨ 텔레비전을 보다가 잠이 들었어요. (= I was watching television and then I fell asleep.)

15. 집에 오고 있었어요. 친구를 만났어요.

⇨ 집에 오다가 친구를 만났어요. (= On my way home, I met a friend. / While coming home, I bumped into a friend.)

Section III - Complete the Dialogue

16.

A: 왜 이거 골랐어요? = Why did you choose this?

B: 계속 고민하다가 이게 제일 싸서 골랐어요. = I thought so hard (about it), and then I chose this because this was the cheapest.

17.

A: 어제 집에 혼자 있었어요? = Were you by yourself at home yesterday?

B: 혼자 있다가 너무 무서워서 친구를 불렀어요. = I was by myself, and then I called my friend to come over because I was too scared.

18.

A: 선생님한테 뭐 물어봤어요? = What did you ask your teacher?

B: 수학 문제를 풀다가 너무 어려워서 물어봤어요. = I asked (him/her) because the math question was too difficult while I was solving it.

19.

A: 어서 오세요. = Welcome.

B: 안녕하세요. 지나가다가 옷이 너무 예뻐서 들어왔어요. = Hello. I came in because I thought the clothes were really pretty while I was passing by.

20.

A: 요즘 어떻게 지내요? = How have you been these days?

B: 계속 아르바이트하다가 너무 힘들어서 최근에 그만뒀어요. = I had a part-time job for a while, and then I quit recently because it was too tiring.

Section IV - Listening Comprehension

A: 늦어서 죄송해요. (= I'm sorry I'm late.)

B: 뭐 21. 하다가 이렇게 늦게 왔어요? (= What took you so long?)

A: 지하철에서 22. 졸다가 잘못 내렸어요. (= I got off at the wrong station because I nodded off.)

Lesson 10

Section I - Vocabulary

1. b
2. a
3. c
4. d
5. c
6. d
7. a
8. a

Section II - Conjugation Practice I

9. 민호가 "이따가 전화할게."라고 했어. (= Minho said, "I will call you later.")

10. 수정이가 "수업 시작하기 전에 올게."라고 했어. (= Sujeong said, "I will come back before the class starts.")

11. 두준이가 "나는 아무거나 줘도 돼."라고 했어. (= Dujun said, "You can give me anything.")

12. 슬기가 "나는 아무 데나 괜찮아."라고 했어. (= Seulgi said, "I am okay/fine with any place.")

13. 공명이가 "나는 여름보다 겨울이 훨씬 더 좋아."라고 했어. (= Gongmyeong said, "I like winter much more than summer.")

14. 하나가 "이 드라마 좀 재밌네."라고 했어. (= Hana said, "This drama is quite good/entertaining.")

Section III - Conjugation Practice II

15. 공짜라고 말하다 = to say that (something) is free of charge

   ⇨ 공짜가 아니라고 말하다 = to say that (something) is not free of charge

16. 한국 사람이라고 말하다 = to say that (someone) is Korean

   ⇨ 한국 사람이 아니라고 말하다 = to say that (someone) is not Korean

17. 내 지갑이라고 말하다 = to say that (something) is my wallet

   ⇨ 내 지갑이 아니라고 말하다 = to say that (something) is not my wallet

18. 범인이라고 말하다 = to say that (someone) is a criminal

   ⇨ 범인이 아니라고 말하다 = to say that (someone) is not a criminal

19. 일 등이라고 듣다 = to hear that (someone) is the first place winner

⇨ 일 등이 아니라고 듣다 = to hear that (someone) is not the first place winner

20. 선물이라고 듣다 = to hear that (something) is a present

⇨ 선물이 아니라고 듣다 = to hear that (something) is not a present

Section IV - Listening Comprehension

A: 주연 씨, 내일 21. 휴가라고 들었어요. (= Joo-yeon, I heard that you are off tomorrow.)

B: 네, 맞아요. 친구랑 놀이공원 가요. (= Yes, that's right. I will go to the theme park with my friend.)

A: 아! 친구도 내일 22. 휴가라고 했죠? (= Ah! You said that your friend is also off tomorrow, right?)

B: 네. 그 친구도 내일 쉬어요. (= Yes, she is also off tomorrow.)

Lesson 11

Section I - Vocabulary

1. e

2. d

3. f

4. i

5. h

6. a

7. b

8. g

9. j

10. c

Section II - Conjugation Practice

11. 태희 씨가 너무 예뻐서 보자마자 반했어요. (= Tae-hee was really pretty, so I fell in love with her as soon as I saw her.)

12. 다리가 너무 아파서 지하철을 타자마자 앉았어. (= My legs were really sore, so I sat down as soon as I got on the subway.)

13. 너무 놀라서 그 소식을 듣자마자 규리 씨한테 전화했어요. (= I was really surprised, so I called Gyuri as soon as I heard the news.)

14. 그 책이 너무 재미있어서 다 읽자마자 친구한테 추천했어요. (= The book was really great, so I recommended it to my friend as soon as I finished reading it.)

15. 그 식당이 인기가 너무 많아서 점심시간 되자마자 달려갔어요. (= The restaurant was really popular, so I ran (to the restaurant) as soon as my lunch break started.)

16. 노래가 좋아서 인기가 많은 것 같아요. (= I think the song is popular because it is good.)

17. 공부를 열심히 해서 일 등 한 것 같아요. (= I think I ranked first because I studied hard.)

18. 아직 안 일어나서 전화를 안 받는 것 같아요. (= I think he/she isn't answering my phone call because he/she hasn't gotten up.)

19. 제가 핸드폰을 계속 떨어뜨려서 고장 난 것 같아요. (= I think my phone stopped working because I dropped it repeatedly.)

20. 오늘 날씨가 너무 추워서 손님이 별로 없

는 것 같아요. (= I think there are not that many customers because the weather is too cold today.)

Section III - Listening Comprehension

21. 이 중에서 아무거나 골라도 돼요? (= Among these, can I pick just any?)

22. 어제 너무 피곤해서 집에 가자마자 아무것도 못 하고 바로 잠들었어요. (= Yesterday I was so tired, so as soon as I got home, I couldn't do anything and just fell asleep right away.)

23. 날씨가 더워서 사람들이 별로 안 온 것 같아요. (= I think not that many people came because the weather is hot.)

Lesson 12

Section I - Vocabulary

1. c
2. f
3. d
4. g
5. h
6. a
7. b
8. e

Section II - Translation Practice

9. 이소라라는 가수
10. 이종욱이라는 야구 선수

11. 김지은이라는 학생
12. 김밥 천국이라는 식당
13. 배두나라는 배우
14. 최경은이라는 사람
15. 운명이라는 것
16. "뭐가 제일 어려워요?"라는 질문

Section III - Vocabulary

17. f
18. c
19. e
20. b
21. a
22. d

Section IV - Comprehension

23. 싸이(PSY)의 강남스타일이라는 노래 들어 봤어요? (= Have you listened to the song called Gangnam Style by PSY? or Have you heard of the song called Gangnam Style by PSY?)

24. 주말에 올드보이(Oldboy)라는 영화를 봤어요. (= I watched the movie called Oldboy on the weekend.)

25. "괜찮아요."라는 말은 여러 가지 뜻이 있어요. (= The expression "괜찮아요" has many meanings.)

26. TalkToMeInKorean.com(톡투미인코리안닷컴)이라는 웹사이트 알아요? (= Do you know the website called TalkToMeInKorean.com?)

27. 내일 알렉스라는 친구가 놀러 올 거예요.

(= Tomorrow, my friend named Alex will come hang out.)

28. 선현우라는 선생님이 한국어를 가르치고 있어요. (= The teacher named Hyunwoo Sun is teaching Korean.)

Section V- Listening Comprehension

29. 공부라는 것은 재미없으면 오래 할 수 없어요. (= Studying is something that you can't do for a long time if it's not interesting.)

Lesson 13

Section I - Vocabulary

1. 회사(會社): company
2. 회사원(會社員): employee, worker
3. 회의(會議): meeting
4. 회의실(會議室): meeting room, conference room
5. 회식(會食): get-together dinner, company dinner
6. 회계(會計): accounting
7. 회비(會費): (membership) fee, (membership) dues
8. 회원(會員): member, membership
9. 회화(會話): conversation
10. 사회(社會): society
11. 국회(國會): National Assembly
12. 대회(大會): competition, tournament
13. 교회(敎會): church
14. 동호회(同好會): club, society

Section II - Comprehension

15. c
16. c
17. b
18. d
19. b

Section III - Listening Comprehension

A: 석진 씨, 회비 20. 냈어요? (= Seokjin, have you paid your membership fee?)

B: 아, 얼마죠? (= Ah, how much is it?)

A: 3만원이요. (= 30,000 won.)

B: 아, 지금 현금이 21. 없네요. 내일 22. 줄게요. (= Oh, I don't have cash with me right now. I will give it to you tomorrow.)

Lesson 14

Section I - Vocabulary

1. c
2. g
3. e
4. a
5. f
6. d
7. h
8. b

Section II - Conjugation Practice

9. 10월 되니까 확 추워졌어요. (= As it became October, it became dramatically colder.)

10. 집이 좁으니까 큰 침대는 못 사요. (= The house is small, so I/we can't buy a big bed.)

11. 사람이 한 명도 없으니까 무서워요. (= There is nobody (here), so I'm scared.)

12. 화장을 진하게 하니까 다른 사람 같아요. (= Since you put on heavy makeup, you look like a different person.)

13. 키가 크니까 옷이 잘 어울리는 것 같아요. (= Since you are tall, I think the clothes suit you well.)

14. 게임을 좋아하니까 좋은 컴퓨터가 필요한가 봐요. (= He/she loves games, so I guess he/she needs a good computer.)

Section III - Comprehension

15. 너무 기뻐서 울었어요. (= I was so pleased that I cried.)

16. 배고프니까 빨리 밥 먹으러 가요. (= I'm hungry, so let's hurry and go eat.)

17. 지루하니까 그만 볼까요? (= It's boring, so shall we stop watching?)

18. 비가 많이 와서 옷이 다 젖었어요. (= It rained a lot, so my clothes got all wet.)

19. 사람들이 다 나갔으니까 청소할까요? (= Now that everyone is gone, shall we clean up?)

20. 의사 선생님이 친절해서/친절하니까 좋아요. (= The doctor is kind, so I like him/her.) (Both are possible. If the listener is aware of the fact that the doctor is kind, 친절하니까 is more natural. If the listener doesn't

know about it, 친절해서 is more natural.)

21. 이 동네가 너무 시끄러워서/시끄러우니까 이사 갈 거예요. (= This neighborhood is too noisy, so I will move away.) (Both are possible. If the listener is aware of the fact that the neighborhood is noisy, 시끄러우니까 is more natural. If the listener doesn't know about it, 시끄러워서 is more natural.)

22. 다른 학생들 공부하니까 조용히 하세요. (= Other students are studying, so please be quiet.)

Section IV - Listening Comprehension

23. 지금 바쁘니까 나중에 전화해 주세요. (= I am busy now, so please call me later.)

24. 오늘은 피곤하니까 우리 영화 내일 봐요. (= I am tired today, so let's watch the movie tomorrow.)

25. 더우니까 에어컨 켤까요? (= It's hot, so shall we turn on the air conditioner?)

Lesson 15

Section I - Vocabulary

1. this

2. I, me ("that" is also possible)

3. coffee

4. by any chance

5. cold

6. any, what, which

7. problem

Section II - Conjugation Practice

8. 누구라도 = anyone

9. 어디라도 = anywhere

10. 언제라도 = anytime

11. 하루라도 = even just one day

12. 잠시라도 = even just a little while

13. 한 명이라도 = at least one person

Section III - Fill in the Blank

14. 뭐라도 마셔요. = Drink something at least.

15. 그거라도 주세요. = At least give me that.

16. 사고라도 났어요? = Did you get into an accident or what?

17. 과자라도 먹을래요? = Would you like a snack at least?

18. 이렇게라도 해야 돼요. = I should at least do this.

19. 내일 영화라도 볼래요? = Do you want to watch a movie or something tomorrow?

Section IV - Listening Comprehension

여: 왜 이렇게 젖었어요? = Why are you so wet?

남: 지금 밖에 비 진짜 많이 와요. 혹시 수건 있어요? = It is pouring outside. Do you have a towel by any chance?

여: 수건이 없네요. 휴지라도 줄까요? = I don't have one. Do you want some tissues at least?

20. c

21. d

Lesson 16

Section I - Vocabulary

1. to sleep

   잔다

2. to bake

   굽는다

3. to sell

   판다

4. to be pretty

   예쁘다

5. to be, to exist

   있다

6. to not be, to not exist

   없다

7. to be good

   좋다

8. to pass by

   지나간다

9. to come

   온다

10. to invite

    초대한다

Section II - Paraphrasing

11. 오늘 날씨 좋아. ⇨ 오늘 날씨 좋다! (= The weather is good today!)

12. 여기 강아지 있어. ⇨ 여기 강아지 있다! (=

There is a puppy here!)

13. 저기 기차 지나가. ⇨ 저기 기차 지나간다! (= Over there, there is a train passing by!)

14. 전화 와. ⇨ 전화 온다! (= The phone is ringing!)

15. 그럼 나는 여기서 기다릴게. ⇨ 그럼 나는 여기서 기다린다. (= Then I will wait here, okay?)

16. 나 먼저 갈게. ⇨ 나 먼저 간다. (= I'm leaving now, okay?)

17. 다음에는 너 초대 안 할게. ⇨ 다음에는 너 초대 안 한다. (= Next time, I won't invite you, okay?)

18. TV 안 볼 거지? 끌게. ⇨ TV 안 볼 거지? 끈다. (= You are not going to watch TV, are you? I'm turning it off, okay?)

Section III - Reading Comprehension

19. c
20. d

Section IV - Listening Comprehension

21. 어? 저기 내 친구들 온다! (= Huh? My friends are coming from over there!)

22. 전화가 안 돼요. 어? 다시 된다! (= The phone is not working. Huh? It's working again!)

23. 우와! 이거 좋다! (= Wow! This is good!)

Lesson 17

Section I - Vocabulary

1. d
2. i
3. e
4. h
5. j
6. f
7. c
8. b
9. g
10. a

Section II - Comprehension

11. 민수 씨가 여름에 스페인으로 여행 간다고 했어요. (= Minsoo said that he will travel to Spain in the summer.)

12. 경은 씨가 주로 도서관에서 공부한다고 했어요. (= Kyeong-eun said that she usually studies at the library.)

13. 진영 씨가 가사 외우는 것이 힘들다고 했어요. (= Jinyeong said that he found it hard to memorize the lyrics.)

14. 유진 씨가 머리가 너무 길어서 덥다고 했어요. (= Yujin said that she felt hot because her hair was too long.)

15. 석훈 씨가 선글라스를 안 쓰니까 눈이 부시다고 했어요. (= Seokhoon said that his eyes were blinded (by the light) because he did not wear sunglasses.)

16. 지연 씨가 내일 떠난다고 했어요. (= Jiyeon

said that she would leave tomorrow.)

Section III - Contraction Practice

17. 비가 온다는 이야기 (= a story in which someone says that it rains)

18. 축하한다는 메시지 (= a message saying that he/she congratulates me)

19. 결혼한다는 소식 (= news that he/she is getting married)

20. 춥다는 사람 (= a person/people who said that it is cold)

21. 재미있다는 소문 (= a rumor that it is fun/enjoyable)

22. 고맙다는 말 (= a word saying thank you)

Section IV - Listening Comprehension

A: 석진 씨, 이사 <u>23. 간다고</u> 들었는데, 맞아요? (= Seokjin, I heard that you will move. Is that correct?)

B: 네. (= Yes.)

A: 언제 이사 가요? (= When are you moving out?)

B: 다음 달 15일에 이사 가요. (= I am moving out on the 15th next month.)

A: 아, 어디로 이사 <u>24. 간다고</u> 했죠? (= Oh, where did you say you were moving to?)

B: 행복동으로 이사 가요. (= I am moving to Haengbok-dong.)

A: 아, 그 동네 <u>25. 좋다는</u> 소문 들었어요. (= Ah, I heard a rumor that the area is good.)

Lesson 18

Section I - Vocabulary

1. to eat

   먹는지

2. to buy

   사는지

3. to play, to hang out

   노는지

4. to untie, to solve

   푸는지

5. to be big

   큰지

6. to be pretty

   예쁜지

7. to be small

   작은지

8. to be narrow

   좁은지

Section II - Conjugation Practice

9. 이거 뭔지 알아요? = Do you know what this is?

10. 뭐가 좋은지 몰라요. = I don't know which one is good.

11. 문제가 있는지 물어보세요. = Ask (them) if there is a problem.

12. 이 사람 누군지 알아요? = Do you know who this person is?

13. 이거 괜찮은지 봐 주세요. = See if this is okay.

14. 어떤 메뉴가 인기가 많은지 알려 주세요. =

Let me know which item on the menu is popular, please.

Section III - Comprehension

15. 이 금이 진짜 금인지 <u>아닌지</u> 알고 싶어요. (= I would like to know whether or not this gold is real gold.)

16. 안에 사람이 있는지 <u>없는지</u> 모르겠어요. (= I can't tell whether or not someone is inside.)

17. 답이 맞는지 <u>안 맞는지</u> 확인해 보세요. (= Check whether or not the answer is correct.)

답이 맞는지 <u>틀리는지</u> 확인해 보세요. (= Check whether the answer is correct or incorrect.) is also possible.

18. 내일 우리 만날 수 있는지 <u>없는지</u> 알고 싶어요. (= I would like to know whether or not we can meet tomorrow.)

19. 우리 숙소가 넓은지 <u>좁은지</u> 아직 몰라요. (= We don't know yet whether our accommodation is big or small.)

우리 숙소가 넓은지 <u>안 넓은지</u> 아직 몰라요. (= We don't know yet whether or not our accommodation is big.) is also possible.

Section IV - Listening Comprehension

여: 석진 씨, 제 컴퓨터가 이상해요. 뭐가 문제인지 좀 봐 줄래요? = Seokjin, my computer is weird. Can you look at it to see what is wrong?

남: 네. 이제 될 거예요. 한번 해 보세요. = Okay.

Now, it will work. Try it.

여: 우와! 이제 된다! 고마워요. 뭐가 문제였어요? = Wow! It works now! Thanks. What was the problem?

남: 잘 모르겠어요. 그냥 껐다가 켜니까 됐어요. = I am not sure. I just rebooted it and it worked.

20. b

21. d

Lesson 19

Section I - Vocabulary

1. b

2. b

3. b

4. b

5. a

6. a&b

7. a

Section II - Conjugation Practice I

8.

민호: "저쪽 길로 가세요." (= "Go that way, please." or "Walk on that street, please.")

나: "민호 씨가 저쪽 길로 가라고 했어요." (= "Minho told me to go that way." or "Minho told me to walk on that street.")

9.

수정: "신발 벗고 들어오세요." (= "Take off your

shoes and come in, please.")

나: "수정 씨가 신발 벗고 들어오라고 했어요."

(= "Sujeong told me to take off my shoes
and come in.")

10.

지은: "피자 시키세요." (= "Order pizza,
please.")

나: "지은 씨가 피자 시키라고 했어요." (= "Jieun
told me to order pizza.")

11.

서현: "조용히 하세요." (= "Be quiet, please.")

나: "서현 씨가 조용히 하라고 했어요." (= "Seo-
hyeon told me to be quiet.")

12.

동욱: "너무 더우면 말하세요." (= "Please tell
me if you feel too hot.")

나: "동욱 씨가 너무 더우면 말하라고 했어요."

(= "Dongwook told me to tell him if I feel
too hot.")

Section III - Conjugation Practice II

13.

경민: "걱정하지 마세요." (= "Please don't
worry.")

나: "경민 씨가 걱정하지 말라고 했어요." (=
"Kyeongmin told me not to worry.")

14.

윤지: "피아노 치지 마세요." (= "Please don't
play the piano.")

나: "윤지 씨가 피아노 치지 말라고 했어요." (=
"Yoonji told me not to play the piano.")

15.

정석: "불 켜지 마세요." (= "Please don't turn
on the light.")

나: "정석 씨가 불 켜지 말라고 했어요." (=
"Jeongseok told me not to turn on the
light.")

16.

진영: "뛰지 마세요." (= "Please don't jump/
run.")

나: "진영 씨가 뛰지 말라고 했어요." (= "Jinyeong told me not to jump/run.")

17.

효린: "사진 찍지 마세요." (= "Please don't take
a picture.")

나: "효린 씨가 사진 찍지 말라고 했어요." (=
"Hyorin told me not to take a picture.")

Section III - Listening Comprehension

여: 현우 씨가 어디로 오라고 했어요? = Where
did Hyunwoo tell you to go?

남: 현우 씨 집으로 오라고 했어요. = He told
me to come to his house.

여: 몇 시까지 오라고 했어요? = What time did
he tell you to come by?

남: 여섯 시까지 오라고 했어요. = He told me to
come by 6 o'clock.

18. 현우 씨 집 (Hyunwoo's house)

19. 여섯 시 or 6시 (6 o'clock)

Lesson 20

Section I - Vocabulary

1. c
2. k
3. a
4. g
5. b
6. m
7. i
8. f
9. e
10. h
11. d
12. l
13. j

Section II - Conjugation Practice

14. 지금 바쁘니까 말 걸지 마세요. (= I'm busy now, so don't talk to me.)

15. 이거 화장품이니까 먹지 마세요. (= This is makeup, so don't eat it.)

16. 모기 들어오니까 창문 열지 마세요. (= Mosquitoes will come in, so don't open the window.)

17. 마이크 또 쓸 거니까 아직 반납하지 마세요. (= I/We will use the microphone again, so don't return it yet.)

18. 늦을 거니까 기다리지 마세요. (= I will be late, so don't wait (for me).)

19. 내일 비 온다고 하는데 행사 취소할까요? (= (Someone) says that it will rain tomorrow, so shall I/we cancel the function/event/ceremony?)

20. 지금 길이 많이 막힌다고 하는데 지하철 타고 갈까요? (= (Someone) says that traffic is now really backed up, so shall we take the subway?)

21. 주연 씨가 늦는다고 하는데 저희 먼저 출발할까요? (= Jooyeon says that she will be late, so shall we leave first?)

22. 전화해 보니까 배달이 안 된다고 하는데 제가 직접 가서 사 올까요? (= I called them, and they said that delivery is not available, so shall I go buy it and bring it in person?)

23. 지금 그 식당 앞에 줄이 길다고 하는데 다른 식당으로 갈까요? (= (Someone) says that the line is long in front of the restaurant now, so shall we go to another restaurant?)

24. 오늘 만나려고 했는데, 갑자기 일이 생겨서 못 만났어요. (= I was going to meet (someone), but something came up, so I couldn't meet him/her/them.)

25. 도시락 싸 오려고 했는데, 늦게 일어나서 못 싸 왔어요. (= I was going to bring lunch, but I got up late, so I couldn't pack my lunch.)

26. 동영상 찍으려고 했는데, 폰 배터리가 없어서 못 찍었어요. (= I was going to film a video, but my phone battery was low, so I couldn't film.)

27. 더 돌아다니려고 했는데, 다리가 너무 아파서 못 돌아다녔어요. (= I was going to

get around more, but my legs hurt, so I couldn't get around.)

28. 오늘은 꼭 강아지랑 산책하려고 했는데, 집에 너무 늦게 들어가서 산책 못 했어요. (= I was going to take a walk with my dog today come what may, but I got home too late, so I couldn't take a walk.)

Section III - Listening Comprehension

29. 지금 주연 씨가 바빠서 못 간다고 하는데, 저라도 갈까요? (= Jooyeon says she can't go because she's busy now, so if you don't mind me going instead, shall I go?)

30. 어제 친구랑 영화 보려고 했는데, 영화관에 사람이 너무 많아서 영화를 못 봤어요. (= I was going to watch a movie with a friend yesterday, but there were too many people, so we couldn't watch the movie.)

31. 그거 비밀이니까 아직 아무한테도 말하지 마세요. (= It's a secret, so don't tell anyone yet.)

Lesson 21

Section I - Vocabulary

1. to invite

2. to call (out)

3. who

4. to wait

5. to press

6. how

7. to tell, to let someone know

Section II - Contraction Practice

8. 너를 ⇨ 널

9. 나를 ⇨ 날

10. 겨울을 ⇨ impossible

11. 친구를 ⇨ 친굴

12. 사람을 ⇨ impossible

13. 선생님을 ⇨ impossible

14. 누구를 ⇨ 누굴

Section III - Comprehension

15. 절 초대해 주세요. ⇨ 저를 초대해 주세요. (= Please invite me.)

16. 여길 어떻게 알았어요? ⇨ 여기를 어떻게 알았어요? (= How did you find out about this place?)

17. 뭘 기다리고 있어요? ⇨ 뭐를 기다리고 있어요? (= What are you waiting for?)

18. 이걸 누구한테 줘야 돼요? ⇨ 이거를 누구한테 줘야 돼요? (= To whom should I give this?)

19. 어딜 보고 있어요? ⇨ 어디를 보고 있어요? (= Where are you looking?)

Section IV - Listening Comprehension

20. 누가 저를 불렀어요? (= Who called me?)

21. 뭘 살 거예요? (= What are you going to buy?)

22. 어디를 눌러야 돼요? (= Where should I press?)

Lesson 22

Section I - Vocabulary

1. 음식(飲食): food
2. 식당(食堂): restaurant
3. 음식점(飲食店): restaurant
4. 식사(食事): meal
5. 식탁(食卓): (dining) table
6. 식품(食品): food item, groceries
7. 간식(間食): snack
8. 후식(後食): dessert
9. 과식(過食): overeating, excessive eating
10. 시식(試食): sample of food, food sampling
11. 분식(粉食): flour-based food
12. 외식(外食): to eat out, to dine out

Section II - Comprehension

13. d
14. a
15. c
16. d
17. d

Section III - Listening Comprehension

A: 경화 씨, 방금 전에 18.식사했는데, 또 간식 먹어요? (= Kyung-hwa, you just ate, and you are eating snacks again?)

B: 네. 드실래요? (= Yes. Do you want some?)

A: 아니요. 19. 괜찮아요. 저는 배불러요. (= No. I am okay. I am full.)

Lesson 23

Section I - Vocabulary

1. h
2. d
3. g
4. k
5. b
6. a
7. j
8. c
9. e
10. i
11. f

Section II - Comprehension

12. a (-(으)려나 보다 cannot be used for adjectives except when talking about the weather. So, choice D sounds natural.)

13. c (You sound more certain of your statement when using -(으)ㄹ 것 같다.)

14. b (-(으)려나 보다 is a way of expressing your assumption about a FUTURE action.)

15. c (-(으)려나 보다 cannot be used for adjectives except when talking about the weather. So, choice A sounds natural.)

16. c (The other ones are all irregular verbs.)

Section III - Paraphrasing

17. 지금 시작하려고 해요. ⇨ 지금 시작하려나 봐요.

(I am going to start now. / They are about to

start now. ⇨ It looks like (someone) is about to start now.)

18. 다 같이 들어오려고 해요. ⇨ 다 같이 들어오려나 봐요.

(They are all going to come in together. ⇨ It looks like they are all going to come in together.)

19. 카페 문을 닫으려고 해요. ⇨ 카페 문을 닫으려나 봐요.

(I am planning to close the café. / (Someone) is about to close the café. ⇨ It looks like (someone) is going to close the café.)

20. 중국 음식 시키려고 해요. ⇨ 중국 음식 시키려나 봐요.

(I am going to order Chinese food. / (Someone) is about to order Chinese food. ⇨ It looks like (someone) is about to order Chinese food.)

21. 공부를 열심히 하려고 해요. ⇨ 공부를 열심히 하려나 봐요.

(I am going to study hard. / (Someone) is going to study hard. ⇨ It looks like (someone) is going to study hard.)

22. 가족하고 여행을 가려고 해요. ⇨ 가족하고 여행을 가려나 봐요.

(I am planning to go on a trip with my family. ⇨ It looks like (someone) is planning to go on a trip with his/her family.)

Section IV - Listening Comprehension

A: 수영 씨, 점심 싸 왔어요? = Soo-yeong, did you bring your lunch?

B: 아니요. = No.

A: 지금 현우 씨 점심 시키려나 봐요. 같이 시키세요. = It looks like Hyunwoo is about to order his lunch. Order something with him.

B: 아, 현우 씨 중국 음식 시키려나 봐요. 저는 나가서 김밥 사 올게요. = Ah, Hyunwoo seems to be ordering Chinese food. I will go out to get some kimbap.

23. b. No
24. b. No. He didn't order his lunch yet.

Lesson 24

Section I - Vocabulary

1. c
2. f
3. j
4. i
5. g
6. a
7. e
8. b
9. h
10. d

Section II - Translation Practice

11. 커피 말고 차
12. 이거 말고 저거 (이것 말고 저것 is also possible.)

13. 차가운 물 말고 뜨거운 물

14. 이 노래 말고 다른 노래

15. 사탕 말고 초콜릿

16. 거기 말고 여기

Section III - Conjugation Practice

17. 그쪽으로 가지 말고 이쪽으로 오세요. (= Don't go that way and come this way.)

18. 저 기다리지 말고 먼저 가세요. (= Don't wait for me and leave first.)

19. 지금 사지 말고 조금만 기다리세요. (= Don't buy it now and wait just a little while.)

20. 늦지 말고 일찍 오세요. (= Don't be late and come early.)

21. 숨기지 말고 얘기하세요. (= Don't hide it and tell me.)

22. 미루지 말고 미리미리 하세요. (= Don't put it off and do it in advance.)

23. 걱정하지 말고 그냥 해 보세요. (= Don't worry and just give it a try.)

Section IV - Listening Comprehension

A: 경화 씨, 커피 한 잔 줄까요? = Kyung-hwa, would you like a cup of coffee?

B: 아니요. 커피 말고 차 주세요. = No. I would like some tea, not coffee.

24. 차 (tea)

A: 주연 씨, 경은 씨가 밥 먹지 말고 기다리라고 했어요? = Jooyeon, did Kyeong-eun tell you not to eat and wait for her?

B: 아니요. 기다리지 말고 먼저 먹으라고 했어요. = No, she didn't. She told me not to wait for her and eat first.

25. b

Lesson 25

Section I - Vocabulary

1. to be small

작아요

작은 편이에요

2. to be easy

쉬워요

쉬운 편이에요

3. to be big

커요

큰 편이에요

4. to be busy

바빠요

바쁜 편이에요

5. to be expensive

비싸요

비싼 편이에요

6. to be fast

빨라요

빠른 편이에요

7. to be good at

잘해요

잘하는 편이에요

8. to be quiet

조용해요

조용한 편이에요

9. to play the piano well, to be good at
   playing the piano
   피아노를 잘 쳐요
   피아노를 잘 치는 편이에요

10. to come often
    자주 와요
    자주 오는 편이에요

Section II - Comprehension

11. 이 길보다 저 길이 안 막혀요. ⇨ 이 길에 비
    해서 저 길이 안 막히는 편이에요.
    (That road is less congested than this road.
    ⇨ Compared to this road, that road tends
    to be less congested.)

12. 다른 가게보다 이 가게가 싸요. ⇨ 다른 가게
    에 비해서 이 가게가 싼 편이에요.
    (This store is cheaper than other stores.
    ⇨ Compared to other stores, this store is
    pretty cheap.)

13. 수학은 저보다 석진이가 잘해요. ⇨ 수학은
    저에 비해서 석진이가 잘하는 편이에요.
    (Seokjin is better at math than me. ⇨
    Compared to me, Seokjin is quite good at
    math.)

14. 저는 드라마보다 영화를 많이 봐요. ⇨ 저는
    드라마에 비해서 영화를 많이 보는 편이에요.
    (I watch movies more than dramas. ⇨ I
    tend to watch movies a lot compared to
    dramas.)

15. 빨간색 구두보다 검은색 구두가 잘 팔려요.
    ⇨ 빨간색 구두에 비해서 검은색 구두가 잘

팔리는 편이에요.
(The black shoes sell better than the red
shoes. ⇨ Compared to the red shoes, the
black shoes sell pretty well.)

16. 다른 브랜드 옷보다 이 브랜드 옷이 예뻐요.
    ⇨ 다른 브랜드 옷에 비해서 이 브랜드 옷이
    예쁜 편이에요.
    (The clothes from this brand are prettier
    than the clothes from other brands. ⇨
    Compared to clothes from other brands,
    the clothes from this brand are quite
    pretty.)

Section III - Listening Comprehension

A: 로빈 씨 가족은 다 키가 17. 크시네요. (=
Robin, your family members are all tall.)

B: 그래요? 그렇게 18. 큰 편은 아니라고 생각했
는데. (= Are they? I didn't think they were
that tall.)

A: 저희 가족에 비하면 19. 큰 편이죠. (= Compared to my family, they are all quite tall.)

Lesson 26

Section I - Vocabulary

1. e
2. f
3. j
4. h
5. i
6. b

7. k

8. c

9. g

10. l

11. a

12. d

Section II - Comprehension

13. chicken instead of pheasant = 꿩 대신 닭

14. bread instead of (cooked) rice = 밥 대신 빵

15. a text message instead of a phone call = 전화 대신 문자

16. a camera instead of a computer = 컴퓨터 대신 카메라

17. candy instead of chocolate = 초콜릿 대신 사탕

18.

A: 집에 도착하면 전화할게요. (= I will call you when I arrive home.)

B: 전화 대신 문자 주세요. (= Please send me a text message instead of a phone call.)

19.

A: 아침에 밥 먹었어요? (= Did you eat rice for breakfast?)

B: 밥 대신 빵 먹었어요. (= I ate bread instead of rice.)

20.

A: 밸런타인데이에 초콜릿 받았어요? (= Did you get chocolate on Valentine's Day?)

B: 초콜릿 대신 사탕 받았어요. (= I got candies instead of chocolate.)

21.

A: 한국에는 꿩 대신 닭이라는 속담이 있어요. 알아요? (= There is a proverb called "Chicken Instead of Pheasant" in Korea. Do you know about it?)

B: 아니요. 몰라요. (= No, I don't.)

22.

A: 컴퓨터 샀어요? (= Did you buy a computer?)

B: 아니요. 컴퓨터 대신 카메라 샀어요. (= No. I bought a camera instead of a computer.)

Section III - Conjugation Practice

23.

A: 경화 씨, 벌써 퇴근해요? (= Kyung-hwa, are you already getting off of work?)

B: 네. 하지만 오늘 일찍 가는 대신에, 내일 일찍 와야 돼요. (= Yes. I'm leaving early today, and in return I need to come early tomorrow.)

24.

A: 이것 좀 빌려줄 수 있어요? (= Can you lend me this?)

B: 제가 이거 빌려주는 대신에, 저 영어 공부 도와줘야 돼요. (= I will lend this to you, but you have to help me learn English in return.)

25.

A: 엄마, 밖에 나가서 친구들이랑 놀아도 돼요? (= Mom, can I go outside and hang out with my friends?)

B: 흠… 그럼 지금 노는 대신에, 이따가 공부해

야 돼. 알겠지? (= Hmmm... then, you can hang out now, and in return you need to study later. Okay?)

26.

A: 오늘 밥은 네가 사. (= You buy meals today.)

B: 좋아. 그런데 내가 사는 대신에, 내가 먹고 싶은 것 먹어야 돼. 괜찮지? (= Alright. However, I'm buying, so in return we eat what I want to eat. Sounds okay, right?)

27.

A: 제 머리 이 색으로 염색하면 어떨까요? (= How will I look if I get my hair dyed with this color?)

B: 예쁠 것 같아요. 근데 예뻐지는 대신에 머릿결은 포기해야 돼요. (= I think it will look pretty. However, in return for having pretty hair, you shouldn't except it to be good quality.)

Section IV - Listening Comprehension

남: 민정 씨, 석진 씨한테 전화했어요? = Minjeong, did you call Seokjin?

여: 아니요. 전화 대신 문자 보냈어요. = No. I sent him a text message instead of calling him.

남: 석진 씨는 문자 잘 안 보는 편이니까 전화해 보세요. = Seokjin doesn't usually check his text messages, so give him a call.

여: 네. = Okay.

28. c

29. b

Lesson 27

Section I - Vocabulary

1. f
2. g
3. b
4. i
5. j
6. a
7. e
8. d
9. h
10. c

Section II - Conjugation Practice

11. 있어요. ⇨ 있잖아요.
12. 있었어요. ⇨ 있었잖아요.
13. 알아요. ⇨ 알잖아요.
14. 알았어요. ⇨ 알았잖아요.
15. 추워요. ⇨ 춥잖아요.
16. 추웠어요. ⇨ 추웠잖아요.
17. 말해요. ⇨ 말하잖아요.
18. 말했어요. ⇨ 말했잖아요.
19. 귀여워요. ⇨ 귀엽잖아요.
20. 귀여웠어요. ⇨ 귀여웠잖아요.
21. 재밌어요. ⇨ 재밌잖아요.
22. 재밌었어요. ⇨ 재밌었잖아요.
23. 일요일이에요. ⇨ 일요일이잖아요.
24. 일요일이었어요. ⇨ 일요일이었잖아요.

Section III - Fill in the Blank

25.

A: 우리가 한국에 언제 갔죠? (= When did we go to Korea?)

B: 그때 엄청 추웠잖아요. 겨울에 갔죠. (= Come on, it was very cold at the time! We went there in the winter.)

26.

A: 이 캐릭터는 왜 이렇게 인기가 많을까요? (= Why do you think this character is so popular?)

B: 귀엽잖아요. 안 귀여워요? (= It's because it's cute! Don't you think so?)

27.

A: 어? 왜 빵집이 문을 닫았죠? (= Huh? Why is this bakery closed?)

B: 오늘 일요일이잖아요. (= Come on, today is Sunday.)

28.

A: 이 영상 다시 찍어야 돼요. (= We need to film this video again.)

B: 왜요? (= Why?)

A: 제가 아까 말했잖아요. 소리가 녹음이 안 됐어요. (= I told you earlier. The sound did not get recorded.)

29.

A: 저희 예전 사무실 앞에 큰 중국집 있었잖아요. 지금은 카페로 바뀌었어요. (= You know, there used to be a big Chinese restaurant in front of our old office. Now, it's been changed to a coffee shop.)

B: 아, 정말요? (= Oh, really?)

Section IV - Conjugation Practice

25a.

A: 우리가 한국에 언제 갔지?

B: 그때 엄청 추웠잖아. 겨울에 갔지.

26a.

A: 이 캐릭터는 왜 이렇게 인기가 많을까?

B: 귀엽잖아. 안 귀여워?

27a.

A: 어? 왜 빵집이 문을 닫았지?

B: 오늘 일요일이잖아.

28a.

A: 이 영상 다시 찍어야 돼.

B: 왜?

A: 내가 아까 말했잖아. 소리가 녹음이 안 됐어.

29a.

A: 우리 예전 사무실 앞에 큰 중국집 있었잖아. 지금은 카페로 바뀌었어.

B: 아, 정말?

Section V - Listening Comprehension

A: 다 30.왔지? (= Everyone's here?)

B: 수연이는? (= How about Soo-yeon?)

A: 수연이는 31.바쁘잖아. 안 불렀어. (= Soo-yeon is busy as you know, so I haven't called her.)

B: 그래도 전화 한번 해 보자. (= But still, let's try calling her at least.)

Lesson 28

Section I - Vocabulary

1. k
2. f
3. c
4. e
5. j
6. i
7. a
8. d
9. b
10. g
11. h

Section II - Conjugation Practice

12. 살 수밖에 없다 (= to have no other choice but to buy)
13. 포기할 수밖에 없다 (= to have no other choice but to give up)
14. 좋아할 수밖에 없다 (= can only like)
15. 어려울 수밖에 없다 (= to be obviously expected to be difficult)
16. 비쌀 수밖에 없다 (= to be obviously expensive)
17. 시끄러울 수밖에 없다 (= to be bound to be noisy)

Section III - Comprehension

18.
A: 이 목걸이는 정말 비싸네요. (= Wow, this necklace is very expensive.)
B: 비쌀 수밖에 없어요. 이게 다 다이아몬드예요. (= It's obviously expensive. These are all diamonds.)

19.
A: 가방 새로 샀어요? (= DId you buy a new bag?)
B: 살 수밖에 없었어요. 너무 예쁜데 가격도 저렴했어요. (= I had no other choice but to buy it. It was really pretty and the price was also inexpensive.)

20.
A: 경화 씨, 재민 씨 좋아해요? (= Kyung-hwa, do you like Jaemin?)
B: 당연하죠. 재민 씨는 항상 밝고 친절해서 좋아할 수밖에 없어요. (= Of course. Jaemin is always bright and kind, so I can't help but like him.)

21.
A: 저는 어릴 때 축구 선수였는데 무릎을 다쳐서 축구를 포기할 수밖에 없었어요. (= I was a soccer player when I was young, but I hurt my knees, so I had no other choice but to give up.)
B: 심각한 부상이었나 봐요. (= I assume it was a serious injury.)

22.
A: 이 글은 너무 어려워요. (= This writing is too difficult.)
B: 이건 뉴스 기사여서 어려울 수밖에 없어요. (= This is a news article, so it is obviously expected to be difficult.)

23.

A: 이 집에는 아이들이 굉장히 많네요. (= There are a lot of children in this house.)

B: 네. 그래서 하루 종일 시끄러울 수밖에 없어요. (= Yes. Therefore, it is bound to be noisy all day.)

Section IV - Paraphrasing

24. 어제 밤늦게까지 공부를 해서, 오늘 피곤할 수밖에 없어요. (= I/He/She studied until late last night, so I/he/she's bound to be tired today.)

⇨ 어제 밤늦게까지 공부를 해서, 오늘 안 피곤할 수가 없어요. (= I/He/She studied until late last night, so there is no way that I/he/she cannot be tired.)

25. 미안하지만 이렇게 할 수밖에 없어요. (= I am sorry, but there is no other choice for me but to do it this way.)

⇨ 미안하지만 이렇게 안 할 수가 없어요. (= I am sorry, but there is no way that I can't do it this way.)

26. 그럴 수밖에 없어요. (= It's bound to be that way.)

⇨ 안 그럴 수가 없어요. (= That can't be helped.)

27. 또 이야기할 수밖에 없어요. (= I have no other choice but to talk to them (about this) again.)

⇨ 또 이야기 안 할 수가 없어요. (= There is no way that I can't talk to them (about this) again.)

28. 걱정이 될 수밖에 없어요. (= I'm obviously going to be worried.)

⇨ 걱정이 안 될 수가 없어요. (= There is no way that I won't be worried.)

Section V - Listening Comprehension

A: 나 태환이랑 수영 시합했는데 졌어. (= I had a swimming race against Taehwan, and I lost.)

B: 네가 29. 질 수밖에 없지. 태환이는 30. 선수 잖아. (= Of course you lost. Taehwan is a swimmer.)

A: 그래도 평영은 자신 있었는데... (= But I was still confident about my breaststroke...)

Lesson 29

Section I - Vocabulary

1. f

2. d

3. g

4. h

5. a

6. c

7. i

8. b

9. e

Section II - Conjugation Practice

10. 민기 씨가 생일 파티를 할 거라고 했어요. (= Min-ki told me that he was going to have a

birthday party.)

11. 용호 씨가 다음에 다시 올 거라고 했어요. (= Yong-ho said that he would come back another time.)

12. 석원 씨가 오늘 비 올 거라고 했어요. (= Suk-won said that it was going to rain today.)

13. 민수 씨가 카메라 샀다고 했어요. (= Min-soo said that he bought a camera.)

14. 은지 씨가 지갑을 잃어버렸다고 했어요. (= Eun-ji said that she lost her wallet.)

15. 진영 씨가 최근에 이사했다고 했어요. (= Jinyoung said that he moved recently.)

Section III - Fill in the Blank

16. 민호 씨, 감기(에) 걸렸다고 들었는데, 괜찮아요? (= Min-ho, I heard that you caught a cold. Are you okay?)

17. 석진 씨, 컴퓨터가 고장 났다고 들었는데, 고쳤어요? (= Seokjin, I heard that your computer was broken. Have you fixed it?)

18. 주연 씨, 오늘 학교에 안 갔다고 들었는데, 무슨 일 있어요? (= Jooyeon, I heard that you didn't go to school today. Is there something wrong?)

19. 지민 씨, 회사 그만둘 거라고 들었는데, 맞아요? Or 지민 씨, 회사 그만둔다고 들었는데, 맞아요? (= Ji-min, I heard that you will quit your job. Is that true?)

20. 에밀리 씨, 미국으로 돌아갈 거라고 들었는데, 언제 가요? Or 에밀리 씨, 미국으로 돌아간다고 들었는데, 언제 가요? (= Emily, I heard that you will go back to the United States. When are you going?)

21. 경화 씨, 밥 안 먹을 거라고 들었는데, 배 안 고파요? Or 경화 씨, 밥 안 먹는다고 들었는데, 배 안 고파요? (= Kyung-hwa, I heard that you will not have breakfast/lunch/dinner. Are you not hungry?)

Section IV - Listening Comprehension

A: 주연 씨 휴가 언제 22.갈 거라고 했죠? (= Joo-yeon, when did you say you were going on vacation?)

B: 4월에요. (= In April.)

A: 어디로 23.정했다고 했죠? (= Where did you say you chose to go?)

B: 베트남이요. 하노이 갈 거예요. (= Vietnam. I will go to Hanoi.)

Lesson 30

Section I - Vocabulary

1. d
2. i
3. f
4. h
5. g
6. b
7. e
8. a
9. j
10. c

Section II - Matching

11. 벌써 5시니까 이제 곧 해 뜰 거예요. (= Since it is already 5 o'clock, the sun will rise soon.)

12. 혼자 가지 말고 저희랑 같이 가요. (= Don't go by yourself, go with us.)

13. 제가 이거 도와주는 대신에 제 부탁 하나 들어주세요. (= I am helping you with this one, but in return, please do me a favor.)

14. 아직 3시니까 런치 메뉴 시킬 수 있어요. (= Since it is still 3 o'clock, we can order items from the lunch menu.)

15. 다음번에 여기 다시 오면 더 오래 머물고 싶어요. (= When I come here again next time, I would like to stay longer.)

16. 간다는 사람이 없으니까 저라도 갈 수밖에 없어요. (= Since there is no one who said they will go, there is no other way but for me to go.)

Section III - Listening Comprehension

17. 벌써 <u>10시니까</u>, 오늘 가지 말고 내일 가요. (= It is already 10 o'clock, so do not go today and go tomorrow (instead).)

18. 제가 이거 도와주는 대신에, 다음번에 제가 <u>부탁이 있으면</u> 들어줘야 돼요. (= I'm helping you with this one, but in return, you have to help me when I need a favor next time.)

19. 지금은 다른 <u>사람이 없으니까</u> 저라도 갈 수 밖에 없어요. = (There is no one else now, so there is no other way but for me to go there (even though I am not the best person for it).)